Heat Pumps and Electric Heating

Heat Pumps
and Electric Heating

Residential, Commercial,
Industrial Year-Round
Air Conditioning

E. R. AMBROSE

Head, Heating and Air Conditioning Division
American Electric Power Service Corporation

JOHN WILEY & SONS, INC.
New York • London • Sydney

Foreword

I am particularly happy to have the opportunity to write this foreword to *Heat Pumps and Electric Heating* by my colleague of many years, for a number of reasons: it is a revision and an enlargement of *Heat Pumps* coauthored by E. R. Ambrose, Theodore Baumeister, and myself more than eighteen years ago; the progress made in the solution of the many problems that pressed for solution two decades ago to make the heat pump a common, year-round air conditioning system has been substantial, even though much slower than I had anticipated or indeed today have reason to believe was necessary or unavoidable; and, finally, although the heat pump today is too well established to warrant any concern for its future existence, the alacrity with which it ought to be adopted and exploited throughout the energy-using world is prominently missing. And this is hard to explain and be unconcerned about in the light of the developments in energy, and particularly electric energy, which have come forth clearly on the horizon in the past ten years and which were barely visible a decade ago.

The outstanding fact about the electric power industry, which is now in the eighty-third year of its existence, is not its consistently maintained great rate of growth during the past eight decades, but the prospects of its continuing at substantially the same rate for the balance of the century. This has a very important bearing on the availability of the primary energy sources necessary to keep pace with this continuing geometric growth.

Thus, electric energy production in the United States, which in 1920 reached a figure of generation of 39 billion kwhr, by 1960 had increased nearly twenty-fold, to over 750 billion kwhr. This growth is expected to reach 2000 billion kwhr by 1975 and 6000 billion kwhr by the year 2000. In terms of primary energy this has meant a total of over 320 million tons of coal equivalent for the generation of electric energy out of a total energy consumption of 1714 million tons of coal equivalent, or slightly under 19 percent. The growth of electric energy by 1975 to 2000 billion kwhr will mean a primary energy equivalent of 700 million tons of coal per annum out of a total of 2750 million tons covering all energy, or somewhat over 25 percent. By the year 2000, with an energy production of 6000 billion kwhr, the primary energy required for this generation will be 1600 million tons of coal equivalent, or 40 percent of the total.

To take care of the nation's vast growth in total energy requirements in the year 2000 will involve a production of 1200 million tons of coal. This is no mean task for coal to undertake and no mean responsibility to throw on coal, whose all-time maximum production, never again attained since the 1940's, is not very much above 600 million tons of coal. The energy crisis that a total required production of 4000 million tons of bituminous coal equivalent would create would be one of vast proportions but for the fact that atomic energy will in the year 2000 pick up through its contribution to the primary energy pool some 850 million tons of bituminous coal equivalent out of the total of 4000 million required.

There is, however, a small catch here and the catch is in the fact that to date and for the immediate future we have found no way of bringing atomic energy into the service of man except through the electric route. And this means that for atomic energy to be useful and—as is inevitable—to become more and more the principal energy source of our society in the centuries after the second millenium, all our energy utilization will have to be converted more and more to the electrical form.

This is where the heat pump comes in. The heat pump offers a way of completely electrifying all heating requirements in the home and eventually many of the heating requirements in chemical and other industrial processes. It promises to do so with an over-all conversion efficiency equal to or greater than 100 percent, solely by virtue of the ambient heat which the heat pump can make available to any thermal process. From a national interest standpoint, therefore, there cannot be any question that no segment of our economy that can find a way of introducing the heat pump into any area of thermal energy use, both with economic and with other advantage, can afford to overlook the opportunity; this responsibility cuts across our entire society, but particularly our engineering society and at every level: academic, research and development, and industrial.

There are, of course, many other cogent reasons for advancing the application of the heat pump in air conditioning, the principal one of which is that it is a means of giving to human society controlled weather that is flexible, automatic, and capable of precision control. Not only does the heat pump make possible healthier and more enjoyable living; when the system is properly researched, engineered, manufactured, and installed, its use can be highly profitable.

To anyone intrigued by any of these prospects, *Heat Pumps and Electric Heating* ought to offer irresistible reading.

PHILIP SPORN

Member National Academy of Sciences,
Member National Academy of Engineering,
Chairman, System Development Committee, American Electric Power Company

New York
October 1965

Preface

Many advancements have been made in the design and performance of heat pumps and electric space heating equipment during the past twenty-five years. The heat pump, particularly, has advanced from a pioneering effort of a few custom built installations a year to an annual production of more than 85,000 factory-assembled units. I was most fortunate in having been closely associated with various phases of this activity during this period and have experienced some of the disappointments as well as some of the encouragements which seem ever present in such developments.

Included in this book are a number of basic equipment arrangements and application procedures which have been found to be most feasible and acceptable for dependable and practical total electric, year-round comfort air conditioning systems. My background of design and application experience was very useful in the selection of the various operating cycles which were included and in the development of a procedure for comparing and correctly evaluating the relative merits of the several competitive types of heating and cooling systems.

The subject matter in this book is principally confined to certain aspects of arrangement, equipment selection, and application practices of residential, commercial, and industrial heating and cooling systems. It is these which will provide maximum knowledge and assistance to the consulting engineer, architect, and mechanical contractor, to electric utility people and to manufacturer's sales and installation representatives. Basic refrigeration theory and detailed coverage of the design characteristics of the several equipment components such as compressors, motors, throttling and diverting valves, fans, pumps, and electrical equipment have been purposely excluded.

It was thought that these subjects were adequately treated in the many excellent textbooks, the heating and air conditioning trade association handbooks, and the various manufacturers' product manuals.

Considerable improvement has been made, and is still being made, in the design, quality, and adaptability of electric heating and cooling equipment to assure a practical and reliable system. It is my hope that this book will not only provide useful information, but at the same time give some encouragement and conviction to those people associated with various phases of the air conditioning industry in order to cause an accelerated public acceptance of these truly amazing electric heating and cooling systems.

I have made every effort to give proper credit in the text to sources of information, and take this opportunity to express my appreciation and thanks to the numerous manufacturers, trade associations, and authors who were kind enough to grant permission for use of this material.

E. R. AMBROSE

New York
October, 1965

Contents

Heat Pumps and Electric Heating

Chapter 1

Thermodynamic Principles

The heat pump is the name generally applied to a year-round air conditioning system in which refrigeration equipment is employed to supply useful heat to the space during the heating cycle and to abstract unwanted heat from the space during the cooling cycle. When the heat pump operates as a heating system, the heat is taken from the outdoor air, water, or other such low-temperature heat source and delivered, together with the heat equivalent of the work of compression, to the conditioned space. Conversely, when operating as a cooling system, the heat pump abstracts heat from the conditioned space and rejects it together with the heat equivalent of the work of compression to an outside heat sink.

There is no fundamental difference between the well-known vapor-compression refrigeration cycle and the heat pump cycle. Thermodynamically, both systems are heat pumps employing a compressor, condenser, cooling coils or evaporator, throttling valve, controls, and piping in order to absorb heat at a low-temperature level and reject it at a higher temperature level. The main difference between the two systems is the primary objective of the application. A refrigeration installation is concerned with the low-temperature effect produced at the evaporator while the heat pump is concerned with both the cooling effect produced at the evaporator and the heating effect produced at the condenser.

IDEAL HEAT PUMP CYCLE

The Carnot cycle, as shown in Figure 1-1, represents the highest possible performance between two temperatures and is considered the ideal heat pump cycle. In this cycle the refrigerant fluid enters

1

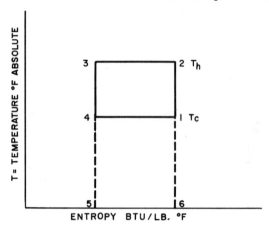

Figure 1-1   Temperature-entropy diagram for the Carnot cycle.

the compressor at point 1. Thermodynamically the sequence consists of:

> Phase 1-2, isentropic compression (constant entropy)
> Phase 2-3, isothermal compression or condensation (constant temperature)
> Phase 3-4, isentropic expansion (constant entropy)
> Phase 4-1, isothermal expansion or evaporation (constant temperature)

The heat absorbed by the system (the refrigerating effect) is represented by Q_c (area 1,4,5,6). The heat rejected by the system is represented by Q_h (area 2,3,5,6). The energy added ideally by the compressor as work to accomplish these effects is represented by $Q_h - Q_c$ (area 1,2,3,4).

RANKINE CYCLE

The Rankine cycle, which assumes irreversible expansion at constant enthalpy through a throttle valve, is generally chosen as more indicative or representative of a vapor-compression refrigeration cycle. Complete description of the Rankine thermodynamic cycle is adequately treated in many refrigeration and air conditioning textbooks. Consequently, the brief review given here will only demonstrate how the cycle is applicable to the heat pump for heating and cooling. Thermodynamically, the Rankine cycle can be illustrated by the temperature-entropy diagram of Figure 1-2. The sequence, after the fluid enters the compressor at point 1, consists of:

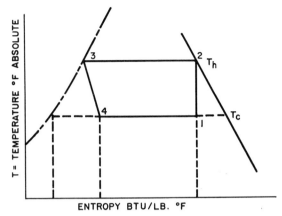

Figure 1-2   Rankine cycle temperature-entropy diagram. Wet compression—no subcooling.

Phase 1–2, compressed isentropically

Phase 2–3, condensed isothermally to liquid at constant pressure and therefore constant temperature

Phase 3–4, expanded irreversibly at constant enthalpy through a throttling valve

Phase 4–1, evaporated isothermally to wet vapor at constant pressure and therefore constant temperature

Tabular and graphical values of enthalpy (h) for the refrigerant are essential for the determination of the Rankine cycle performance. Most convenient in this respect is the Mollier (pressure-enthalpy) chart, as shown in Figure 1-3 for refrigerant R12, Figure 1-4 for refrigerant R22 and Figure 1-5 for R502. A typical operating cycle, giving the amount of heat rejected and the refrigerating effect produced, together with the various changes in the state of the refrigerant, is indicated on the pressure-enthalpy charts. Referring to Figure 1-5 we find the refrigerant enters the compressor slightly superheated at point 1' and is compressed at constant entropy to point 2'. The gas is then desuperheated to point 2 and condensed to liquid at constant pressure (and therefore constant temperature) to point 3. The liquid is expanded, irreversibly, at constant enthalpy through a throttling valve to point 4 and then evaporated to a vapor, at constant pressure and temperature, back to point 1' to complete the cycle.

When the refrigerant properties are available in graphical form as illustrated by Figures 1-3, 1-4, and 1-5, it is usually more practical

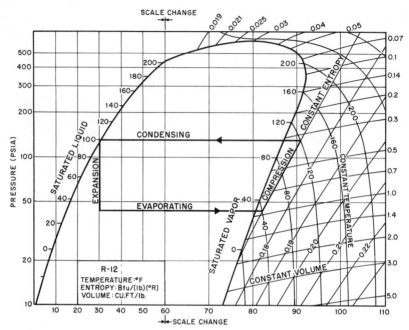

Figure 1-3 Enthalpy (Btu/lb above saturated liquid at −40 F). (E. I. du Pont de Nemours and Co., Inc.)

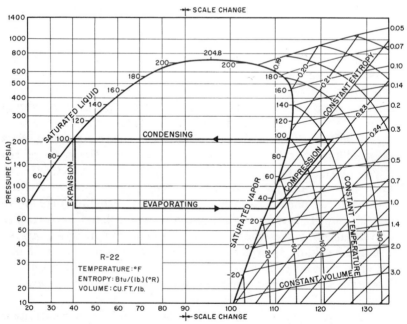

Figure 1-4 Enthalpy (Btu/lb above saturated liquid at −40 F). (E. I. du Pont de Nemours and Co., Inc.)

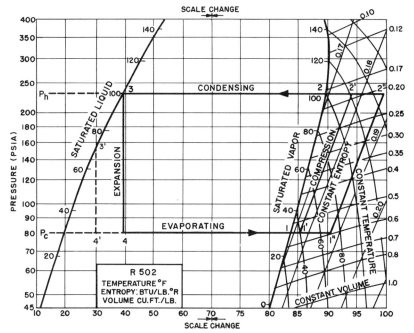

Figure 1-5 Enthalpy (Btu/lb above saturated liquid at -40 F). (E. I. du Pont de Nemours and Co., Inc.)

and accurate to use the following general energy equations for evaluating the work, the heat delivered, and the refrigerating effect obtained with the Rankine cycle:

Work of the Rankine cycle, W (Btu/lb) $= h_h - h_c$ (1-1)

(where h_h and h_c are, respectively, the enthalpy, in Btu per pound, of vapor leaving and entering the compressor)

Heat delivered, Q_h (Btu/lb) in the heat pump cycle

$$= h_2 - h_3 \text{ or } h_h - h_{\text{liq}} \quad (1\text{-}2)$$

(where h_h and h_{liq} are, respectively, the enthalpy in Btu per pound of vapor leaving the compressor and of the liquid leaving the condenser)

Refrigerating effect or heat absorbed by the evaporator

$$= Q_c \text{ (Btu/lb)} = h_1 - h_4 \text{ or } h_c - h_{\text{liq}} \quad (1\text{-}3)$$

(where h_c and h_{liq} are, respectively, the enthalpy of the vapor entering the compressor and of the liquid entering the evaporator)

COEFFICIENT OF PERFORMANCE

An index of the performance of the cycle is the coefficient of performance (cp). By definition, the actual coefficient of performance of a heat pump, during the heating cycle, is equal to the total instantaneous heat output, Q_h, at stated conditions, divided by the heat equivalent of the net work required to produce the effect. During the cooling cycle, the cp is the ratio of the instantaneous refrigeration effect, Q_c, and the heat equivalent of the net work done in producing the effect, or:

$$\text{cp (heating cycle)} = \frac{\text{Heat output, } Q_h}{\text{Work } (Q_h - Q_c)} \tag{1-4}$$

$$\text{cp (cooling cycle)} = \frac{\text{Refrigeration effect, } Q_c}{\text{Work } (Q_h - Q_c)} \tag{1-5}$$

Since the areas representing the energy quantities, Q_h, Q_c, and $(Q_h - Q_c)$ in Figure 1-1 are rectangular, the vertical absolute temperature scale will also serve to express the theoretical coefficient of performance for the Carnot cycle. The maximum heating coefficient of performance for the Carnot cycle, therefore, is the ratio of the absolute temperature, T_h, at which condensation occurs and the temperature difference between the condensation temperature, T_h, and the evaporation temperature, T_c. Similarly, the maximum cooling coefficient of performance is the ratio of the absolute temperature at which evaporation takes place and the temperature difference between the condensation temperature T_h and evaporation temperature, T_c, so that:

$$\text{cp (Carnot heating cycle)} = \frac{T_h}{T_h - T_c} \tag{1-6}$$

$$\text{cp (Carnot cooling cycle)} = \frac{T_c}{T_h - T_c} \tag{1-7}$$

The coefficient of performance of the Carnot cycle is useful as a reference to indicate important influencing factors but can never be remotely approached in practice. This is because isothermal compression or expansion cannot be accomplished practically, and the low mean temperature gradient between the refrigerant and the ambient results in prohibitive equipment size and low mechanical efficiency.

The coefficient of performance (cp) of the Rankine cycle is, therefore, more representative of an actual heat pump operating cycle. Using equations 1-1, 1-2 and 1-3, it is possible to write the following:

$$cp \text{ (Rankine heating cycle)} = \frac{h_h - h_{liq}}{h_h - h_c} \qquad (1\text{-}8)$$

$$cp \text{ (Rankine cooling cycle)} = \frac{h_c - h_{liq}}{h_h - h_c} \qquad (1\text{-}9)$$

The Rankine cycle is less efficient than the Carnot cycle. Accordingly, the Rankine coefficient of performance as given by equations 1-8 and 1-9 will be lower than the Carnot cycle values given by equations 1-6 and 1-7.

In an actual heat pump system the coefficient of performance varies directly as the compressor suction pressure and inversely as the condensing pressure. The suction pressure, in turn, is determined by the temperature of the heat source, so that the lower the heat source temperature the lower the compressor suction pressure. Similarly, the head pressure or condensing pressure is determined by the heat sink temperature or the temperature of the medium being circulated to the conditioned space.

A comparison of the coefficient of performance at various air heat source and heat sink temperatures for the Carnot cycle, the Rankine cycle and an actual heat pump unit is shown in Figure 1-6. The coefficient of performance of an actual heat pump cycle is lower than the Carnot or Rankine cycles because:

1. Temperature gradients are necessary for the heat transfer from the refrigerant to the heat source and heat sink. During the heating cycle the refrigerant condensing temperature must be about 10 to 20 F higher than the heating medium going to the conditioned space. Also, the refrigerant evaporating temperature must be about 10 to 20 F below the heat source temperature. Similarly, during the cooling cycle the refrigerant evaporating temperature must be about 10 to 15 F below the cooling medium going to the conditioned space and the refrigerant condensing temperature must be about 20 F above the heat sink temperature.

2. Fan power necessary to move the air over the heat transfer surfaces represents about 10 percent of the total energy input to sustain the process.

3. The theoretical compression cycles do not take into consideration compressor volumetric efficiency and departure from the ideal compression cycle.

4. The compressor-motor combination is only 85 to 90 percent

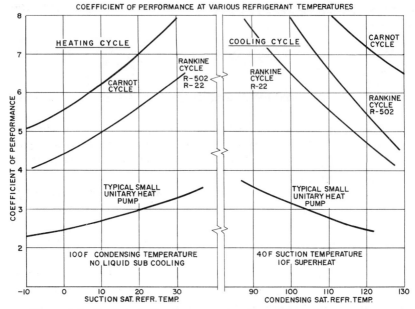

Figure 1-6   Coefficient of performance at various refrigerant temperatures.

efficient. The hermetically sealed refrigerant motor-compressor customarily used adds these motor losses to the refrigerant before compression.

HORSEPOWER

The compressor horsepower per ton of refrigeration can be computed from the work equations (1-1). One ton of refrigeration may be defined as the removal of 200 Btu/min of heat in the evaporator and a horsepower is equal to 33,000 ft-lb/min or 42.41 Btu/min. The pounds of refrigerant circulated per ton-minute is, therefore, equal to

$$\frac{200}{\text{Refrigeration effect } Q_c} \quad \text{or} \quad \frac{200}{h_c - h_{\text{liq}}} \tag{1-10}$$

and

$$W \text{ (Btu per ton-minute)} = \frac{200}{h_c - h_{\text{liq}}} (h_h - h_c) \tag{1-11}$$

Therefore

$$\text{Horsepower (per ton of refrigeration)} = \frac{200}{42.41} \frac{h_h - h_c}{h_c - h_{\text{liq}}} \tag{1-12}$$

VOLUMETRIC EFFICIENCY

The compressor volumetric efficiency, E_v, may be defined as the ratio of the actual volume of gas drawn into the compressor, to the piston displacement.

$$E_v = \frac{\text{Volume of gas at suction condition}}{\text{Piston displacement}} \qquad (1\text{-}13)$$

or

$$E_v = \frac{\text{Weight of gas delivered}}{\text{Weight equivalent of piston displacement}} \qquad (1\text{-}14)$$

The factors influencing the actual E_v are clearance, suction throttling, suction heating, valve leakage and piston ring leakage.

SUPERHEAT VAPOR, SUBCOOL LIQUID

If the refrigerant leaving the evaporator or heat sink surface is in a superheated condition (point 1′ or 1″ of Figure 1-5) the refrigerating effect and the work of compression are both increased. The probable net effect is that the coefficient of performance will increase very slightly, if at all, and at the higher suction temperatures may even decrease.

Increasing the vapor temperature of the gas entering the compressor by means of a gas-liquid heat exchanger increases proportionally the temperature rise in the compressor head. This temperature increase in the compressor head, caused mainly by the low transfer rate of the superheated vapor, results in an increased discharge pressure and an additional load on the condenser. With hermetically sealed compressors, a larger suction heating effect than indicated by the heat transfer in the exchanger may be expected if the gas is brought through the crankcase or near the motor windings. The effect of pressure drop through the suction side of the gas-liquid heat exchanger cannot be overlooked, since it causes the compressor to operate at a lower suction pressure which, in turn, decreases the refrigeration capacity.

Even though the gas-liquid heat exchanger may not be justified on the basis of increased cycle efficiency, there are some circumstances which make its use desirable.

1. Installations using expansion valves require 8 to 10 degrees of superheat in the evaporator for satisfactory performance. The use of a heat exchanger may make it unnecessary to use the evaporator for superheating the gas, thus increasing the refrigeration

capacity of the coil. This is particularly true for water cooler applications. The expansion valve operation is also improved by maintaining a better control of the hunting of the valve and by reducing the amount of liquid refrigerant carried back to the compressor by entrainment.

2. Many installations will have uninsulated suction lines outside the conditioned space. If the heat gain of such suction lines cannot be avoided, a heat exchanger can be used to increase the refrigerating effect by superheating the gas which, in turn, subcools the liquid refrigerant. The necessity for insulating the suction line is then eliminated.

3. The liquid-suction heat exchanger can be used also to subcool liquid refrigerant to prevent flash gas in the liquid line. Such an application is necessary when excessive pressure drops are present in the liquid line, because of functional and static head losses in the piping between the liquid receiver and the evaporator.

Liquid-suction interchangers are to be used with caution in R22 refrigerant systems. Excessive superheating of suction gas must be avoided with this refrigerant to prevent excessive compressor discharge temperatures.

SUBCOOLING LIQUID BY EXTERNAL FLUID

If the liquid leaving the condenser is subcooled below the saturation temperature (from point 3 to 3′ in Figure 1-5) the enthalpy after the throttling operation would be some point such as 4′. In this case, the refrigerating effect and the useful heat output per pound of liquid circulated are increased without any change in the work of compression.

In contrast to the disadvantages resulting from superheating the suction gas, the subcooling of the liquid refrigerant will always improve the heat output and the coefficient of performance of the system during the heating cycle. With subcooling the horsepower per ton decreases and the coefficient of performance increases as the liquid refrigerant temperature from the condenser decreases. The subcooling of the liquid can be accomplished best by means of an external fluid cooler. An example of such a cooler is a ventilation air-refrigerant coil application. During the colder weather the ventilation air passes over the external surface of the coil and the liquid refrigerant through the tubes. In this manner the ventilation air is preheated by subcooling the liquid refrigerant. This type of application is more thoroughly discussed in Chapter 4.

REFRIGERANTS

The physical, and electrical properties, together with the velocity of sound, performance, leak detection, and effect on material construction of the more common refrigerants can be found in any good refrigeration handbook. Consequently, this coverage of refrigerants will be limited to a discussion of the more desirable features and properties for heat pump applications.

Perhaps the most important factors influencing the choice of refrigerants, for use in comfort air conditioning installations, are the physical properties. These properties include flammability, danger from explosion, toxicity, odor, acidity, reactivity with air, oil, water, and other substances, corrosiveness, lubricating characteristics, and chemical stability. In a refrigerant even a slight degree of toxicity, irritation to the senses, or odor could be a deterrant to selection. A characteristic pungent odor, which may be harmless, could constitute a serious potential threat in the form of a panic hazard.

The choice of the type and design of compressor will be influenced by the compression ratio and the refrigerant volume factors. It is desirable to have the evaporator pressure as high as is feasible while keeping the condensing pressure as low as possible. The compression ratio determines the volumetric efficiency of a positive displacement unit and influences the number of stages required in a centrifugal or axial flow unit. Also, the compression ratio in centrifugal compressors is affected by the vapor density. The density is related to the molecular weight of the gas as well as to the operating temperature and pressures.

Refrigerant characteristics change with operating temperatures. Some refrigerants are advantageous for low refrigeration systems between −40 and 20 F, others are more favorable in the air conditioning range of 20 to 40 F. It may also be found that a particular refrigerant is better for a cooling machine than for a heating machine. Maximum allowable compressor discharge temperature varies depending on design, but is usually fixed at 275 to 350 F. It has been estimated that the ratio of chemical reaction of a system doubles with each 20 F increase. On this basis a system with a useful life of 20 years, at a given temperature level, would be reduced to a probable life of 5 years by a 40 F increase in discharge temperature.

Because of a difference in flow rates and specific heat, the discharge temperatures for some refrigerants at a given set of conditions are substantially lower than others. The discharge temperature of a hermetic motor compressor with R502 for example, at −40 F saturated suction temperature, will be about 34 F lower than with R22. The motor winding temperature, as well as the crankcase and oil temperatures, will also be cooler with R502 because of the lower average temperature of the cooling fluid. This favorable condition results from the greater mass velocity of the refrigerant, which in turn causes a correspondingly higher heat transfer rate between the winding and refrigerant vapor. The differences are smaller in the ideal theoretical cycle than in the actual compressor cycle, which has both motor and compressor inefficiencies.

Other properties which influence the refrigerant selection are:

1. Viscosity of the liquid and vapor.
2. Specific heats. Liquid heat capacity is involved as the condensed liquid is cooled to evaporator temperature.
3. Electrical properties. They are especially important in hermetic systems.
4. Horsepower per ton of refrigeration. This is about the same for all refrigerants.
5. Plastic materials. Not all can be used, but they are important. The effect of R22 on plastic is generally somewhat more severe than R12.
6. Rankine coefficient of performance. This can be effectively used for comparison of relative efficiencies.
7. Enthalpy gain of the refrigerant. This must be fully utilized for useful refrigeration effect. Maximum capacity gain in some gas is achieved at the higher return gas temperature which means suction line heat exchangers can be used. R502 is an example of such a refrigerant.
8. Piston displacement per ton. Required piston displacement per ton materially influences the compressor design and size. The greater the density and the enthalpy the higher the capacity at a given compressor displacement.

REFERENCES

ASHRAE Guide and Data Book, Fundamentals and Equipment for 1965 and 1966 Chap. 19, Refrigerants, American Society of Heating, Ventilating and Air Conditioning Engineers.

Du Pont "Freon" Technical Bulletin RT-31, "Freon" 502 Refrigerant, E. I. du Pont de Nemours and Co., Inc., "Freon" Products Div., Wilmington, Delaware, (19888), April 1964.

Faber, Oscar, The Value of Heat with Special Reference to the Heat Pump, *Proceedings Institute Mechanical Engineering,* **154,** 144–178 (September 1946).

Soumerai, Henri, Evaluation of Refrigerant 502 in Integral Horsepower Commercial Refrigeration Compressors, *ASHRAE Journal,* January 1964.

Spofford, W. A., *Performance of Packaged Heat Pump Units,* A Symposium Bulletin on Heat Pump Performance, American Society of Heating, Refrigeration, and Air Conditioning Engineers, January 1959.

Chapter 2

Heat Sources and Sinks, Storage Systems, Domestic Water Heaters

The choice of the heat source and sink is of primary significance because of the heat pump's dual function of providing heating and cooling. Under winter or heating conditions heat is abstracted from the heat source and delivered to the conditioned space. Under summer or cooling conditions the heat is removed from the conditioned space and discharged to the heat sink. The utilization or choice of the most practical medium for a particular application will be influenced by many factors, such as geographic location, climatic conditions, initial cost, availability, and suitability. Practically any form of low level heat is readily applicable to the heat pump cycle, but the majority of the systems use outdoor air or well water as the source and sink. Other possible media include the ground, solar energy, and industrial processes.

AIR

Outdoor air offers a universal, inexpensive, and abundant heat source-sink for the heat pump, and its popularity has been rapidly increasing in all sections of the country. This medium is used almost exclusively on residential installations and is fast becoming the principal selection for the commercial and industrial applications.

The selection or design of the air source heat pump components is affected by the outdoor temperature variation in a given locality and by the formation of frost on the heat source coil. Many localities experience wide fluctuations in outdoor air temperatures and the structure heating requirements are of course greatest when the outdoor temperatures are the lowest. Frost may form on an outdoor air coil if the surface temperature is 32 F or lower, and periodic defrosting is necessary. This frost, if allowed to accumulate, will ultimately

14

interfere with the heat transfer. The capacity deficiency of an air source heat pump at the low outdoor temperatures can be neutralized by fully utilizing all methods for conserving heat, by proper system design, and by using supplemental resistance heat for the short, infrequent cold spells during the winter period.

Methods and procedures for handling these and the many other influencing factors will be found in Chapters 3 and 4.

WATER

Water from wells, lakes, rivers, and manufacturing processes, where the temperature is too low for direct utilization, is often a very satisfactory heat source-sink providing:

1. It is chemically suitable, is not of an excessively corrosive nature, and does not require extensive treatment or the use of expensive metals. Well water is often available in dependable quantities at depths of 150–600 ft and at favorable temperatures, usually above 50 F throughout the year. Unfortunately, it is becoming increasingly difficult to obtain a dependable supply of trouble-free water in many parts of the country.

2. Its disposal after use and the local codes and restrictions do not constitute a difficult problem. In many instances, return wells are necessary or storm sewers are subject to a user's tax. Such conditions may make the system prohibitive, for the heat pump is a once-through system and large quantities of water are required.

3. The uncertainty of finding a sufficient quantity, at a given location, and the cost of drilling and maintenance do not detract from its use. It is to be noted that the cost of developing well water supply is frequently prohibitive for residential and small commercial installations. In certain industrial applications, use may be made of waste process water as a heat source, as for example, warm discharge water from laundries or from large industrial condensers.

GROUND

The earth has not been found to be a practical and dependable heat source and sink. A considerable amount of activity on this subject took place in the early 1940's, including the laboratory and field investigation of many installations, which ranged in performance from a few hours of continuous operation to 5 years of intermittent operation. These investigations gave the following results and conclusions:

1. Embedded heat transfer surfaces could be horizontal tubular bundles or grids and vertical tubes or tanks. The horizontal grids

varied in length from 88 to 2200 ft of ⅞ in. or 1⅛ in. OD tubes whereas the vertical heat transfer surfaces varied from 50 ft long monotubes to 5 ft diameter tanks.

Frequently, the horizontal pipes were spaced 3 to 6 ft apart and submerged below the surface 3 to 6 ft. A lower depth might be preferred, but excavation cost required a compromise. Mean, undisturbed ground temperature generally followed the average annual mean climatic temperature of the given area.

Usually it was concluded that an average safe selection would be 200 to 400 ft of ⅞ in. to 1⅛ in. OD tubing per ton of refrigeration effect, buried 4 ft apart at a depth of 4 ft. To insure continued contact between the coil and ground material, the space directly around the coil was sometimes back-filled with sand. In spite of this precaution, it has been found that after a few years the space between the earth and pipe gradually increased until the surface was no longer satisfactory as a heat sink. This adverse effect does not occur when the surface acts as a heat source probably because the moisture in the ground migrates and freezes around the pipe to fill the void.

2. Compressors, used in the investigations, varied in size from ¾ to 7½ hp.

3. Heat transfer media circulated within the buried heat transfer surfaces included brine solution, antifreeze, R12 and R22 refrigerant and water.

4. Operating temperatures of the heat transfer surface varied during the heating cycle from 15 to 46 F, and during the cooling cycle from 80 to 130 F.

5. The heat transfer rates for the horizontal grids varied during the heating cycle from 1.68 to 5.15 Btuh (ft)(°F), and during the cooling cycle from 0.64 to 1.3 Btuh (ft)(°F). For the vertical surfaces the heat transfer rates varied during the heating cycle from 1.07 to 6.72 Btuh (sq ft)(°F), whereas for cooling the rate (on one test) was 1.47 Btuh (sq ft)(°F).

SOLAR

Considerable interest has been manifested in solar energy as a heat source, either on a primary basis or in combination with other sources. Many ingenious, direct-utilization solar collectors for comfort heating have been described in the literature. Usually these collectors have single, double, or triple glass covers to provide maximum retention of the heat and minimum heat loss to the ambient air. Only a relatively few of these collectors however, have been installed to date because of their complexity and high first cost.

The heat pump offers several possibilities for overcoming some of the present handicaps facing the direct-utilization collector, because of its inherent ability to absorb the solar heat at a relatively low collector temperature. Operating at these lower collector temperatures reduces the transmission losses. The reduction, in turn, materially increases the collector efficiency. At the same time, these low collector temperatures permit obtaining a larger percentage of the lower intensity solar energy occurring on cloudy days and during early morning and late afternoon hours. The principal attraction for using solar radiation in this manner is the possibility of providing a higher temperature heat source than the other more common sources.

Research and development in the use of solar energy as a heat source for heat pumps have been concerned with both the direct and indirect types of applications. In the direct system, direct expansion refrigerant tubes are attached to the solar collector, usually of the flat plate type. The indirect system circulates water or air as an intermediate fluid through the solar collector. Any of the basic heat pump cycles described in Chapter 3 can be adapted to the use of solar energy. For example, a collector can be added to an air-to-air heat pump cycle in such way that the solar energy will serve only as an outdoor-air preheater. Other possibilities are to use solar energy exclusively as the heat source, or alternately with the outdoor air. When an indirect type system is desired, either an air-to-water or a water-to-water heat pump cycle can be employed.

It is apparent that a practical and effective heat pump system employing solar energy must have either an alternate heat source or some means of heat storage during periods of insufficient solar radiation. The average number of hours of sunshine, as well as the percentage of possible sunshine hours, vary widely in the United States, ranging in December from 45 hr and 16 percent for Erie, Pennsylvania, to 254 hr and 82 percent for Yuma, Arizona. Even under the most favorable conditions, therefore, solar energy can be expected only about 34 percent of the total heating hours.

A possible heat pump system for using the solar and sky radiation as a heat source is shown in Figure 2-1. During the heating cycle the compressor delivers the high-pressure, high-temperature refrigerant to the condenser-cooler, where it is liquefied by giving up its latent heat of condensation to the water in the storage tank. The refrigerant liquid then changes into a low-temperature, low-pressure gas in the solar collector by obtaining the needed latent heat of vaporization from solar and sky radiation. The surface temperature

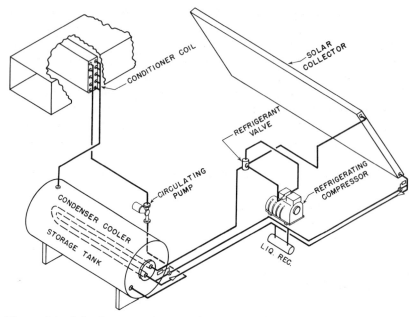

Figure 2-1 Solar heat pump system for year-round air conditioning. (Sporn and Ambrose, *Proceedings, World Symposium on Applied Solar Energy,* November 1955.)

of the solar collector can be maintained at about 60 F or lower, and that of the condenser-cooler at a refrigerant condensing temperature of about 110 F or higher. The warm water from the storage tank in turn is circulated to the conditioner coil to provide the required heating.

The solar collector used as a heat source for winter heating can easily be adapted to serve as a heat sink for summer cooling. The position of the four-way refrigerant valve is changed so that the compressor will first deliver the refrigerant to the solar collector (which is now the condenser), then to the condenser-cooler (which is the cooler). The high-temperature, high-pressure gas is condensed in the collector, giving up the latent heat of condensation to the ambient, and the resulting liquid refrigerant is changed into a low-temperature, low-pressure gas in the condenser-cooler, taking the heat of vaporization from the water in the storage tank. The resulting cold water can then be circulated through the conditioner coil to provide cooling.

With such a solar collector application the rain, wind, solar and sky radiation, and the outdoor air can all be made to serve as a heat source and heat sink. Outdoor air can be circulated over the collector during the heating cycle to provide a heat source during those periods when solar heat is unavailable. The same forced circulation system can also be used during the cooling system if gravity circulation over the collector is insufficient to maintain reasonable condensing temperatures.

STORAGE

During the severe outdoor temperature periods the maximum electric demand of a heat pump or resistance type heating system invariably coincides with the daytime peak demand of the other electric equipment. In many instances it may be possible to use heat from a storage tank to supplement or replace the basic heating system in order to reduce the demand during the critical coincident periods. The storage tank can be recharged during mild weather (when excess heat pump capacity is available) and/or during off-peak periods when the electric utility has excess generating capacity available. Using this off-peak storage makes it possible not only to reduce the daytime electric demand, but also to improve materially the seasonal performance factor of the equipment. Several electric utilities offer incentive heating rates to encourage the use of electric energy for recharging the storage tank during specified periods when excess electric generation facilities are available.

There are a number of possible heat storage combinations with the heat pump and/or with resistance-type electric heating, depending upon the type of application. Figure 2-1 shows a combination storage tank and condenser-cooler unit which uses solar energy as a heat source or sink. In this case, during the heating cycle the water is raised to a sufficiently high temperature level by the heat pump and stored, so that it can be directly used for space heating. Similarly, during the cooling cycle, the stored, chilled water can be used for space cooling.

It may be considered very uneconomical to employ condenser side (high-temperature) storage for a heat pump solar collector system if, for example, it were necessary to collect all of the available radiation during an average month of January. In such a design the heat pump equipment would probably be sized for a refrigeration load of 275 Btuh per sq ft of collector, which is the typical maximum rate of solar radiation, incident upon a south-facing vertical surface for a cloudless January day in most parts of the United States. Another possibility is to employ low-temperature storage. For this arrangement, water or a chemical material could be stored in a suitable tank at 50 to 60 F to serve as a heat source for the heat pump.

In this case the required refrigeration compressor capacity could frequently be reduced by about 80 percent below that required for high-temperature storage based on the maximum available radiation. Such a comparison, however, is often misleading because it would seldom if ever be practical to base the refrigeration equipment selection on an instantaneous heat source which occurs infrequently and is of short duration. In practical heat pump designs, as explained in Chapter 4, the compressor, condenser, and evaporating surfaces are generally sized for the summer design cooling load and not for the maximum heating load.

Solar energy is only one of many possibilities for using heat storage to supplement the daily output to meet peak demand. There are a number of other widely different heat storage materials and methods being used or contemplated for the immediate future. These storage materials are generally classified as either a latent heat or a sensible heat process. In a latent heat process, the addition or extraction of heat actually causes a phase change, such as from solid to liquid, from liquid to gas, or vice versa. The sensible heat process, in contrast, experiences a rise or fall in the temperature of the substance. Examples of sensible heat material include water (between the freezing and boiling points), crushed rock, iron ore, solid masonry, and other such high-density material.

Latent Heat Storage. Many materials have some capacity to absorb heat when changing from a solid to a liquid. Ordinary ice, changing to water, is a good example of a potential low-temperature storage medium. An acceptable and satisfactory heat storage material, however, must have a relatively high latent heat value per unit volume and the absorption and release must occur within predictable limits. Many materials have the disadvantage of subcooling, delayed change of state, or decomposition through time and repeated cycles. Also, most of the available materials are unacceptable because of cost, corrosiveness, instability, or unavailability.

Chemical storage, which falls within the latent heat classification, has been receiving some attention during the past few years because of its attractive possibilities for storing large quantities of heat per unit volume. Recent explorations indicate that fused sodium hydroxide and calcium oxide show some promise. The potential offered by such a storage medium in comparison with other common materials is indicated by Table 2-1.

Sensible Heat Storage: Water. Up to the present, water has probably been used more extensively than any of the other storage materials. When the large space requirements of the storage tank

TABLE 2-1   Comparison of Various Materials for 100 MBtu Storage

	Type	Operating Temp Range °F	Net Weight Lbs	Net Volume Cu Ft	Relative Net Volume %*	Volumetric Heat Capacity Btu/Cu Ft	Material Cost $
Sodium Hydroxide	Inorganic Fusion Material	275–950	211.8	2.0	12.7	50000	11.00
Sodium Nitrite	Inorganic Fusion Material	275–590	425.0	3.4	21.6	29400	40.00
Ammonium Nitrate	Inorganic Fusion Material	275–400	947.5	7.95	50.6	12550	30.40
Sulfur	Inorganic Fusion Material	200–650	1162.0	9.1	58.0	11000	29.10
Glycerin	Organic Liquid	110–545	340.0	4.8	30.6	20800	88.60
Diethylene Glycol	Organic Liquid	110–460	471.0	6.3	41.3	15200	71.50
Humble Therm "500"	Organic Liquid	110–550	383.0	8.8	56.0	11360	35.50
Ethylene Glycol	Organic Liquid	110–360	670.0	9.6	61.1	10400	9.65
Dow Therm A	Organic Liquid	110–476	605.0	11.2	71.3	8900	181.80
Parafin Wax	Organic Fusion Material	110–605	256.0	6.5	41.4	15400	16.70
Lithium Hydride	Organic Fusion Material	200–1256	47.1	1.3	8.28	77000	450.00
Water-Atmospheric Pressure	Liquid - Sensible Heat Only	110–212	980.0	15.7	100.0	6370	
Iron-Steel	Solid - Sensible Heat Only	150–950	1135.0	2.32	14.8	43100	
Concrete	Solid - Sensible Heat Only	150–950	463.0	3.31	21.1	30200	8.00
Brick	Solid - Sensible Heat Only	150–950	625.0	5.2	33.1	19200	

$$* \text{ Relative volume } (\%) = \frac{\text{Net volume of material}}{\text{Net volume of water at 212 F}} \times 100$$

The relative volume comparisons are somewhat misleading, because of the thermal insulation requirements to keep stand-by losses to a minimum. The higher temperature storage material will have a corresponding increase in amount of insulation which can easily double the overall size of the containers.

From Comstock and Wescott, Inc., Development of a Practical Heat Storage System for Edison Electric Institute (unpublished).

can be accommodated in a practical manner water will undoubtedly continue to be used for some time, particularly for the smaller installations, because of the lower first cost. The practical upper limit of unpressurized water storage systems will probably be in the neighborhood of 400,000 Btu with a storage volume of about 100 cu ft.

One of several ways of using water storage in connection with electric heating system is illustrated in Figure 2-2. This type of application can be used with either heat pumps or direct electric heating systems. When combined with a heat pump, the water in a low-pressure storage system (operating at about 15 psig, 250 F) would be heated by means of resistance type elements during the night or other off-peak periods. In this design the heat pump during the day would supply the base load and be supplemented by the stored heat to obtain the most acceptable coincident demand and load factor for the electric power generation system. The same procedure could also be followed where only a resistance-type heating

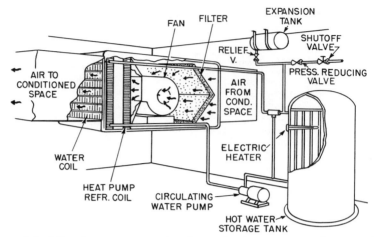

Figure 2-2 Off-peak water storage using electrical resistance as a supplement to heat pump system. (Ambrose, Off-Peak Electric Heating, *Air Conditioning, Heating, and Ventilating,* July 1961.)

system was used. In this case the storage tank medium could be charged with a sufficient quantity of heat, during the off-peak periods, to supply up to 100 percent of the daytime requirements.

Sensible Heat Storage: High-Density Material. Electric heating units, employing high-density storage material, has attractive possibilities. This type of storage material has the advantage of a wide temperature range to provide a considerably increased storage capacity per unit volume over that obtained with water.

Falling within this category are the concrete block type (as illustrated in Figure 2-3) or the high-density metal units, such as cast iron, which have been extensively promoted in several European countries. These units are designed for individual room application, as contrasted with the central plant type of system generally used with water storage. Direct electric heating elements raise the temperature of this storage material to about 400 to 600 F during the off-peak periods. This stored heat, in turn, is released to the room usually by means of automatically operated dampers under control of a room thermostat. The stand-by losses of these heaters are difficult to regulate and will tend to overheat the space during relatively mild weather conditions when little or no heat is required. This overheating will not only cause uncomfortably high ambient temperatures, but will also materially decrease the overall efficiency of the system.

Crushed rock, through which air is allowed to pass, is another

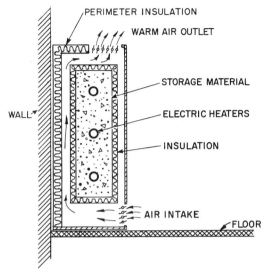

PERIMETER INSULATION

WARM AIR OUTLET

STORAGE MATERIAL

ELECTRIC HEATERS

WALL

INSULATION

AIR INTAKE

FLOOR

Figure 2-3 Sectional view of a suggested unit type of concrete block heaters for off-peak storage. (Ambrose, Off-Peak Electric Heating, *Air Conditioning, Heating, and Ventilating,* July 1961.)

example of high-density storage which has been used to a limited extent in different sections of the United States. This method of storage has found some favor in connection with solar heating, but does not seem to be very attractive for electric resistance heating.

Low-Temperature Floor Storage. Another exceedingly attractive system for electric heating employs the concrete floor as the storage medium. Such installations are particularly attractive for warehouses, storerooms, garages, and similar commercial structures where warm floors are advantageous and where the inherent operating characteristics are acceptable.

This type of low-temperature floor radiant system has a number of design and application advantages. For instance, evenly distributed temperatures are provided, air currents are minimized, and drafts reduced. In addition, the temperature is greatest near the floor and lowest near the ceiling. This is the converse of gravity or forced convection systems which generally have the higher air temperatures at the ceiling. Consequently, the conduction heat loss for a floor radiant system should be less than for the convection types of systems. Also, there is some indication that the natural air infiltration rate is lower with low-temperature radiant systems because of the elimination of the thermal head (or chimney) effect which is prevalent in convection heating.

During the permissible charging periods the concrete floor is
heated to predetermined temperatures which can be scheduled to
vary with the outdoor temperature. Generally, the floor temperature
is allowed to vary between 70 and 75 F at mild outdoor temperatures
and increased to 80 to 85 F when extremely cold weather is being
experienced. Field tests have indicated that heat stored in the concrete will maintain reasonably acceptable temperatures during
the 8 to 10 noncharging hours without excessive drop in surface
temperature.

Electric heating cable or bare metal rods can be used as electric
conductors to heat the concrete. The electric heating cable can be
embedded directly in the concrete or enclosed in a specially designed
housing section which is buried in the floor. The directly embedded
cable, which is equipped with a jacket chemically unaffected by
normal building material, has the advantages of low first cost and
ease of installation. A typical installation of heating cable system
embedded directly in the concrete is shown in Figure 2-4a. The heating cable must be carefully spaced on top of the concrete base, followed by the reinforcing rods and the finished coat of concrete as
shown in Figure 2-4b. After application of the perimeter thermal insulation, the concrete base is poured over the sub-base of gravel,
sand, or other suitable granular material which has been previously
covered with a suitable vapor barrier.

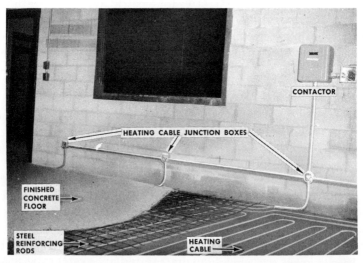

Figure 2-4a Using the concrete floor as the sensible heat-storage medium. The
heating cable is embedded directly in the concrete. (Ambrose, Off-Peak Electric Heating, *Air Conditioning, Heating, and Ventilating*, July 1961.)

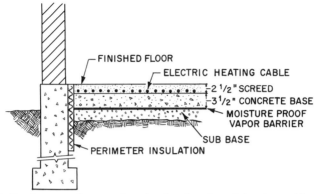

- FINISHED FLOOR
- ELECTRIC HEATING CABLE
- 2 1/2" SCREED
- 3 1/2" CONCRETE BASE
- MOISTURE PROOF VAPOR BARRIER
- SUB BASE
- PERIMETER INSULATION

Figure 2-4b Concrete floor section showing location of heating cable, perimeter insulation, and vapor barrier. (Ambrose, Off-Peak Electric Heating, *Air Conditioning, Heating, and Ventilating,* July 1961.)

Instead of heating cable, bare metal wire or rods can be used to conduct the electric current. Such installations have attractive first cost possibilities because the embedded rods can serve both as heating system and as a substitute for the normally installed reinforcing steel for the concrete. In such installations the floor is generally divided into a number of areas of 1000 to 1200 sq ft. A grid assembly is prefabricated and installed in each floor area, as shown in Figures 2-5a and 2-5b. Electric power at 240 or 480 volts can be supplied through a suitable circuit breaker to the primary side of the transformer where it is stepped down to 30 to 55 volts to feed the metal grid. By variation in the transformer secondary voltage the output of the floor grids can be regulated to provide the desired quantities of heat.

DOMESTIC HEAT PUMP WATER HEATER

In all heat pump designs it is possible to heat water for general domestic use by installing a heat exchanger in the discharge refrigerant line from the compressor. This arrangement takes full advantage of the high superheat temperature of the refrigerant gas and will heat the domestic water whenever the compressor is operating during either the heating or the cooling cycle. Since the hot water usage is not directly related to the heating or cooling requirement, some type of storage must be provided or else a supplemental heating system must be incorporated in the design in order to be assured of an adequate supply of hot water at all times.

Perhaps a more practical arrangement for domestic water heating, particularly for the larger commercial and industrial installa-

Figure 2-5a Method of connecting power cable to a grid assembly which serves both as a heating system and as a substitute for the normally installed reinforcing steel. (Ambrose, Off-Peak Electric Heating, *Air Conditioning, Heating, and Ventilating,* July 1961; Northern State Power Co.)

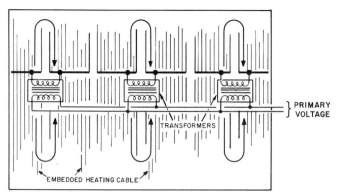

Figure 2-5b Plan showing power wiring for embedded heating grid in concrete floor. (Ambrose, Off-Peak Electric Heating, *Air Conditioning, Heating, and Ventilating,* July 1961.)

tions, is to use a double circuit condenser, similar to that described in Chapter 3 in connection with simultaneous heating and cooling cycles. In a conventional comfort cooling cycle the condenser heat is rejected to the outdoors and an independent source of energy is used to heat the domestic water. In other words, a large quantity of heat is wasted and an equal, if not larger, quantity of energy is used for heating domestic water. One possibility of using a conventional cooling cycle and still recovering the condenser heat is shown in Figure 2-6. Such a recovery system is also applicable to a heat pump using air as the heat source and sink.

Like all heat recovery arrangements, the success and acceptance will depend on the ingenuity of the designer. The solution is not always simple, but there are many installations which are feasible and practical. The important feature of the system shown in Figure 2-6 is either the double circuit condenser which can be generally used in conjunction with a cooling tower or, instead, a refrigerant-water heat exchanger which is used in series with an air-cooled condenser installation. The size and flow arrangement to the storage tank, together with the method of controlling the booster resistance heat, would depend on the particular installation. It is possible in such designs for the condenser to supply 65 percent or more of the domes-

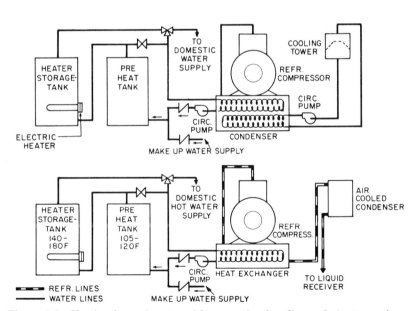

Figure 2-6 Heating domestic water with conventional cooling cycle (water or air can be used as auxiliary heat sink).

tic hot water requirements on an average summer day, 45 percent for the entire summer, and 50 percent for the entire year.

A self-contained heat pump, designed especially for domestic water heating, may be feasible and practical. The heat source for such a domestic water heat pump can be solar energy, ambient air, or any of the other heat sources which have been mentioned previously as suitable for the year-round comfort heat pump units. The equipment arrangement and operating cycle for a domestic water heat pump can be similar to the basic heat pump cycle described in Chapter 3. One of several possible designs and equipment arrangements is shown in Figure 2-7. In this arrangement the high-temperature losses from the compressor and motor shell can be utilized to obtain higher temperature water with no apparent adverse effect on

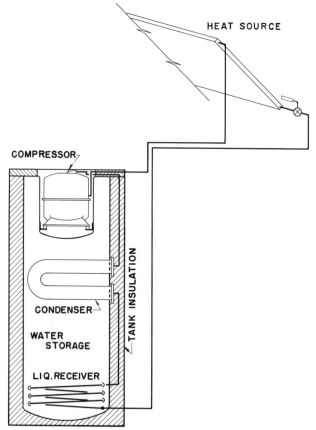

Figure 2-7   Solar heat pump, domestic water heater. (Sporn and Ambrose, *Proceedings, World Symposium on Applied Solar Energy,* November 1955.)

the condenser discharge pressure. One possible advantage is indicated from the results of some exploratory field tests which showed a leaving water temperature of 152 F with a saturated condenser refrigerant temperature of 146 F. The main disadvantage of this particular design is the inaccessibility of the compressor for service and the probable excessive deterioration and corrosiveness of the exposed metal surfaces due to their continuous exposure to the water. For these reasons the compressors are generally located on the outside of the water tank.

The heat pump water heater has never captured the interest of the manufacturers or general public because of the relative higher first cost when compared with an electric resistance or fuel-fired unit. One possible approach to making the heat pump domestic water heater more competitive is to take full advantage of the cooling effect produced by the evaporator to reduce the temperature and the relative humidity of the occupied space. In this way one self-contained package device could be made to perform the triple duty of providing comfort cooling to the space, dehumidifying the air, and heating the domestic water supply.

REFERENCES

Bary, Constantine W., and Joseph F. Paquette, Jr., *Some New Aspects of Electric Heating by Means of Heat Pumps with Supplemental Heat Storage,* Paper CP 62–40, American Institute of Electrical and Electronics Engineers, Winter General Meeting, New York, January 26, 1962.

Dedingfield, John A., Service Hot Water from Air Conditioning Waste Heat, *Air Conditioning, Heating, and Ventilating,* November 1963.

Design, Construction and Testing of a Pilot Model Heat Storage Unit Based on the Heat-of-Fusion System (Final Report), Comstock and Wescott, Inc. for Edison Electric Institute, July 1963.

Feasibility Study of the Heat Pump Water Heater, Report by the Joint AEIC-EEI Heat Pump Committee, *Edison Electric Institute Bulletin,* August 1962.

Haines, J. Thomas, *Heat Storage in Electric Heat Pump and Resistance Heating Systems,* Paper CP 63440, Institute of Electrical and Electronics Engineers, Winter General Meeting, New York, January 27–February 1, 1963.

Healy, C. T., and T. I. Weatherington, Water Heating by Recovery of Rejected Heat from Heat Pumps, *ASHRAE Journal,* 1964.

Ingersoll, L. R., and H. J. Ploss, Theory of the Ground Pipe Heat Loss for the Heat Pump, *ASHVE Transaction,* **54,** 339 (1948).

Jordan, R. C., and J. L. Threlkeld, Availability and Utilization of Solar Energy, *Transactions,* American Society of Heating and Ventilating Engineers, **60,** 177 (1954).

Research Results Concerning Earth as a Heat Source or Sink, prepared by the Joint AEIC-EEI Heat Pump Committee, *Edison Electric Institute Bulletin,* September 1953.

Sporn, Philip, and E. R. Ambrose, Electric Heat, *Air Conditioning, Heating, and Ventilating,* July 1960.

Sporn, Philip, and E. R. Ambrose, The Heat Pump and Solar Energy, *Proceedings, World Symposium on Applied Solar Energy,* Phoenix, Arizona, November 1–5, 1955.

Sporn, Philip, and E. R. Ambrose, Progress Report on a Heat Pump Water Heater, *Heating and Ventilating,* February 1949.

Chapter 3

Basic Designs

The four basic heat pump designs for space heating and cooling employ: (1) air as the heat source-sink and air as the heating and cooling medium, (2) air as the heat source-sink and water as the heating and cooling medium, (3) water as heat source-sink and air as the heating and cooling medium, or (4) water as heat source-sink and water as the heating and cooling medium.

Each of these basic designs can supply the required heating and cooling effect by changing the direction of the refrigerant flow, or by maintaining a fixed refrigerant circuit and changing the direction of the heat source-sink media. A third alternative is to incorporate an intermediate transfer fluid in the design. In this case the direction of the fluid is changed to obtain heating or cooling and both the refrigerant and heat source-sink circuits are fixed. The fixed refrigerant circuit designs, generally referred to as the indirect type of application, are becoming increasingly popular, particularly in the larger capacities.

The basic designs are quite flexible and are readily adaptable to a number of different types of applications. Flow diagrams, together with a brief description, are given for some of the more typical arrangements.

AIR AS THE HEAT SOURCE-SINK AND AIR AS THE HEATING AND COOLING MEDIUM (*Fixed Air Circuits— Refrigerant Flow Reversed*)

An air heat source-sink design using air as the heating and cooling medium, illustrated in Figure 3-1*a*, is by far the most universally used, particularly for the residential and smaller commercial installations having a cooling load of about 25 tons, or lower.

31

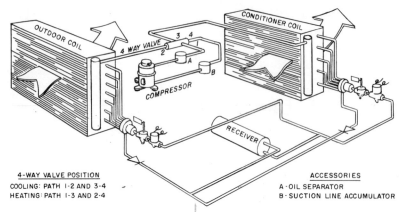

4-WAY VALVE POSITION
COOLING: PATH 1-2 AND 3-4
HEATING: PATH 1-3 AND 2-4

ACCESSORIES
A - OIL SEPARATOR
B - SUCTION LINE ACCUMULATOR

Figure 3-1a   Air as heat source-sink and air as heating and cooling medium (fixed air circuits—refrigerant flow reversed). Throttling valve used to regulate refrigerant effect.

Conventional refrigeration practice can be followed in the selection and arrangement of the equipment, except that it is desirable to have gravity drainage of the liquid refrigerant from the outdoor coils and the conditioner coils to the liquid receiver. The diagram also indicates the probable location of an oil separator in the discharge line, and of a liquid refrigerant–oil accumulator in the suction line. These accessories are generally used on all except the small integral designs in order to assure proper oil return and prevent liquid flood-back to the compressor.

In this design, heating and cooling are obtained by changing the direction of the refrigerant flow. Two fixed independent air circuits are employed, consisting of the outdoor coil circuit and the conditioner coil circuit. During the cooling cycle the four-way valve is positioned to paths 1–2 and 3–4. The compressor delivers the hot compressed refrigerant gas through the four-way valve, path 1–2, to the outdoor coil where it is condensed, giving up the latent heat of condensation to the outside air. From the outdoor air coil the liquid refrigerant flows through the check valve to the liquid receiver and then through the throttling valve to the conditioner coil. In the conditioner coil the liquid refrigerant is changed into a gas that absorbs the heat of vaporization from the air going to the conditioned space. From the conditioner coil the refrigerant gas returns through the four-way valve, path 3–4, to the compressor to repeat the cycle.

During the heating cycle the four-way valve is positioned to paths 1–3 and 2–4. The compressor delivers the hot compressed refrigerant gas through the four-way valve, path 1–3, to the conditioner coil where it is condensed, giving up the latent heat of condensation to the air going to the conditioned space. From the conditioner coil the liquid refrigerant flows through the check valve to the liquid receiver and then through the throttling valve to the outdoor coil. In the outdoor coil the liquid refrigerant changes into a gas that absorbs the heat of vaporization from the outside air. From the outdoor coil the refrigerant gas returns through the four-way valve, path 2–4, to the compressor to repeat the cycle.

Figure 3-1b is a modification of the basic air-to-air heat pump cycle. Two additional check valves and a liquid throttling valve have been added to the basic cycle and the expansion valves, solenoid valves, liquid receiver, and oil separator have been eliminated. In this design the liquid refrigerant is used both to boil the condensed refrigerant from the suction line accumulator and to superheat the suction gas entering the compressor. The throttling valve, C, regulates the refrigerant flow by maintaining a predetermined liquid temperature leaving the condenser. The heat source coil, either the indoor or outdoor coil depending upon the cycle, will operate in a flooded condition because of the absence of an expansion valve. It is important, therefore, that the suction line accumulator be adequately designed to prevent liquid floodback to the compressor.

The main advantage cited for this design is the elimination of the thermostatic expansion valves and the need for a pressure-suction differential to obtain the desired refrigeration effect. Consequently, the system can operate on the cooling cycle at extremely low

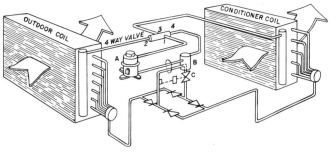

4-WAY VALVE POSITION
COOLING: PATH 1-2 AND 3-4
HEATING: PATH 1-3 AND 2-4

A- COMPRESSOR
B- SUCTION LINE ACCUMULATOR
C- THROTTLING VALVE USED TO REGULATE
REFRIGERATION EFFECT.

Figure 3-1b Air as heat source-sink and air as heating and cooling medium (fixed air circuits—refrigerant flow reversed). (Westinghouse Electric Corporation, Air Conditioning Division.)

outdoor temperatures, and by maintaining the predetermined liquid temperature can operate at reasonably constant head pressures during both the heating and cooling cycle.

AIR AS THE HEAT SOURCE-SINK AND AIR AS THE HEATING AND COOLING MEDIUM (*Fixed Air Circuits— Refrigerant Flow Reversed with Forced Feed Circulation*)

This cycle, illustrated in Figure 3-2, is similar to that described in connection with Figure 3-1, with the exception that forced feed circulation is used. This principle eliminates the need for some of the control equipment and the thermostatic expansion valves at the outdoor coil and the conditioner coil. This cycle is divided into two separate refrigerant circuits, one circuit containing the compressor and the other the refrigerant pump.

For cooling, in one of the circuits the compressor delivers the hot compressed gas through the back-pressure regulator 1 to the outdoor coil where it is condensed, giving up its latent heat to the outdoor air. From the outdoor coil the liquid refrigerant flows through check valve 5 to the high-pressure float regulator and enters the accumulator as a low-pressure liquid gas. From the accumulator the refrigerant gas returns to the compressor. In the other circuit the refrigerant pump 1 circulates the cold liquid refrigerant from the bottom of the accumulator, through check valve 4 to the conditioner coil, where part of the liquid is evaporated, then back through automatic valve 8 to the accumulator.

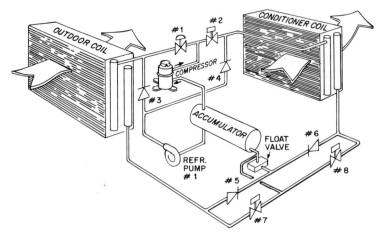

Figure 3-2 Air as heat source-sink and air as heating and cooling medium (fixed air circuits—refrigerant flow reversed with forced feed circulation). (Worthington Air Conditioning Co.)

For heating, in one circuit the compressor discharges the hot compressed refrigerant gas through solenoid valve 2 to the conditioner coil where it is condensed, giving up its latent heat to the air going to the conditioned space. From the conditioner coil the liquid refrigerant drains through check valve 6 to the high-pressure float and enters the accumulator as a low-pressure liquid-gas mixture. From the accumulator the refrigerant gas returns to the compressor. In the second circuit refrigerant pump 1 circulates the cold liquid refrigerant from the bottom of the accumulator through check valve 3 to the outdoor coil where part of the liquid is evaporated, absorbing the heat of vaporization from the outdoor air. From the outdoor coil the cold liquid-gas mixture is returned through automatic valve 7 to the accumulator.

AIR AS THE HEAT SOURCE-SINK AND WATER AS THE HEATING AND COOLING MEDIUM (*Fixed Air and Water Circuits—Refrigerant Flow Reversed*)

Figure 3-3 shows a typical flow diagram of an air heat source-sink design using water as the heating and cooling medium. Heating and cooling are obtained by changing the direction of the refrigerant flow. Two separate fixed circuits are employed, consisting of an outdoor air coil circuit and a water circuit through the condenser-cooler.

The equipment arrangement and operation of this cycle are identical to those given for Figure 3-1 except that a condenser-cooler has been substituted for the air conditioner coil. For the cooling

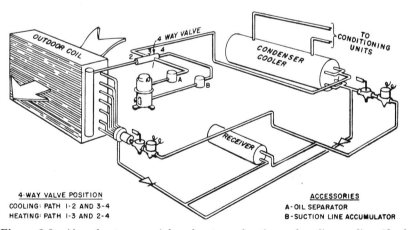

Figure 3-3   Air as heat source-sink and water as heating and cooling medium (fixed air and water circuits—refrigerant flow reversed). Expansion valves used to regulate refrigerant effect.

cycle, the refrigerant flows from the compressor through the four-way valve, path 1–2, the outdoor coil, the check valve, the receiver, the expansion valve, the condenser-cooler, the four-way valve, path 3–4, back to the compressor. The water flowing through the condenser-cooler is cooled by the refrigerant changing from a liquid to a gas. The unwanted heat is rejected from the system through the outdoor air coil by the refrigerant when it condenses from a high-temperature, high-pressure gas to a liquid.

During the heating cycle, the compressor discharges the refrigerant gas through the four-way valve, path 1–3, the condenser-cooler, the check valve, the receiver, the expansion valve, the outdoor coil, the four-way valve, path 2–4, back to the compressor. In condensing from a gas to a liquid the refrigerant heats the water flowing through the condenser-cooler. The heat of vaporization of the refrigerant, in changing from a liquid to a low-pressure gas, is obtained from the air going over the outdoor coil.

WATER AS THE HEAT SOURCE-SINK AND AIR AS THE HEATING AND COOLING MEDIUM (*Fixed Air and Water Circuits—Refrigerant Flow Reversed*)

Figure 3-4 shows a typical flow diagram of a system employing water as the heat source-sink and using air as the heating and cooling medium.

In this cycle, heating and cooling are obtained by changing the

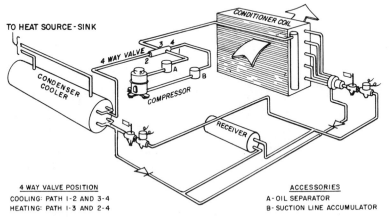

TO HEAT SOURCE - SINK

CONDITIONER COIL

4 WAY VALVE

CONDENSER COOLER

COMPRESSOR

RECEIVER

A

B

4 WAY VALVE POSITION
COOLING: PATH 1-2 AND 3-4
HEATING: PATH 1-3 AND 2-4

ACCESSORIES
A - OIL SEPARATOR
B - SUCTION LINE ACCUMULATOR

Figure 3-4   Water as a heat source-sink and air as heating and cooling medium (fixed air and water circuits—refrigerant flow reversed). Throttling valves used to regulate refrigerant effect.

direction of the refrigerant flow. Two separate fixed circuits are
employed, consisting of a water circuit through the condenser-cooler
and an air circuit over the conditioner coil. During the cooling cycle
the four-way valve is positioned to paths 1–2 and 3–4. The refrigerant
path is from the compressor through the four-way valve, path 1–2,
the condenser-cooler, the check valve, the liquid receiver, the expansion valve, the conditioner coil, the four-way valve, path 3–4, back to
the compressor to repeat the cycle. The refrigerant gas is liquefied
in the condenser-cooler by giving up its latent heat of condensation
to the water and is changed back into a gas in the conditioner coil
by absorbing its heat of vaporization from the air going to the
conditioned space.

During the heating cycle the four-way valve is positioned to
paths 1–3 and 2–4. The refrigerant path is from the compressor
through the four-way valve, path 1–3, the conditioner coil, the check
valve, the liquid receiver, the expansion valve, the condenser-cooler,
the four-way valve, path 2–4, then back to the compressor to repeat
the cycle. Conversely to the process of the cooling cycle, the hot
compressed refrigerant gas from the compressor is liquefied in the
conditioner coil by giving up its heat of condensation to the air going
to the conditioned space, and is changed back into a gas in the condenser-cooler by absorbing the heat of vaporization from the well
water.

During both the cooling and heating cycles well water is circulated by a pump through the preconditioning coil (if used to
precool or to preheat the ventilation air), then through the condenser-cooler to the drain. A complete description of the use of preconditioning coils in such a design is given in Chapter 4.

WATER AS THE HEAT SOURCE-SINK AND WATER AS THE HEATING AND COOLING MEDIUM (*Fixed Water Circuits—Refrigerant Flow Reversed*)

Figure 3-5 shows a typical flow diagram for a water heat source-
sink design using water as the heating and cooling medium. Heating
and cooling are obtained by changing the direction of the refrigerant
flow. Two independent, fixed water circuits are employed. One circuit
consists of the heat source-sink, a condenser-cooler, and the drain.
The second circuit is formed by another condenser-cooler and the
conditioning units in a closed loop.

The flow arrangement is similar to that given in Figure 3-3,
except that a condenser-cooler has been substituted for the outdoor

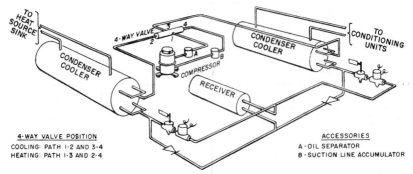

Figure 3-5 Water as heat source-sink and water as heating and cooling medium (fixed water circuits—refrigerant flow reversed). Throttling valves used to regulate refrigerant flow.

coil. With such an indirect system the heating and cooling can be furnished by central plant duct systems or by individual heating and cooling units.

AIR AS THE HEAT SOURCE-SINK AND AN INTERMEDIATE LIQUID AS THE HEATING AND COOLING MEDIUM (*Fixed Refrigerant Circuit—Water Flow Reversed*)

Figure 3-6 shows a typical flow diagram for air source-sink design using a liquid as the heat transfer medium between the surfaces. Heating and cooling are obtained by changing the direction of the liquid flow while maintaining a fixed refrigerant circuit.

During the cooling cycle the three-way valves are positioned to path 1–2. Pump 2 circulates the warm liquid through the outdoor coil, valve *A*, the condenser-liquid receiver, and valve *D*. Pump 1 circulates the cool liquid through the conditioner coil, valve *B*, the cooler, valve *C*, back to pump 1 to repeat the cycle.

During the heating cycle the three-way valves are positioned to path 1–3. Pump 2 circulates the cool liquid through the outdoor coil, valve *A*, the cooler, valve *D*, back to pump 2. Pump 1 circulates the warm water through the conditioner coil, valve *B*, the condenser-liquid receiver, and valve *C*, back to pump 1.

In the air-to-liquid design the compressor delivers the hot compressed gas to the condenser-liquid receiver where it is liquefied, giving up its latent heat of condensation and thus raising the temperature of the circulating liquid. From the condenser the liquid refrigerant flows through the expansion valve to the cooler where it

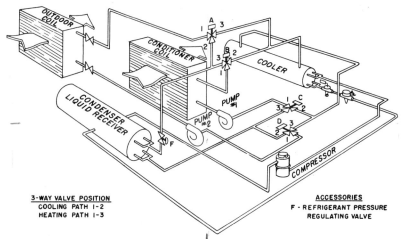

3-WAY VALVE POSITION
COOLING PATH I-2
HEATING PATH I-3

ACCESSORIES
F - REFRIGERANT PRESSURE
REGULATING VALVE

Figure 3-6   Air as a heat source-sink and an intermediate liquid as heating and cooling medium (fixed refrigerant circuits—water flow reversed).

changes into a gas, absorbing the heat of vaporization by reducing the temperature of the circulating liquid, then back to the compressor to repeat the cycle. The liquid used in this design can be of any of the common antifreeze solutions. Selection is a matter of choosing a fluid which has a high specific heat and is chemically inert to the equipment parts.

WATER AS THE HEAT SOURCE-SINK AND WATER AS THE HEATING AND COOLING MEDIUM (*Fixed Refrigerant Circuit—Water Flow Reversed*)

Figure 3-7 shows a typical flow diagram for a water heat source-sink design using water as the heating and cooling medium. Heating and cooling are obtained by changing the direction of the water flow while maintaining a fixed refrigerant circuit.

During the cooling cycle the three-way valves are positioned to path 1–2. The well pump circulates the water through the preconditioning coil to precool the ventilation air. The heat sink water then flows through valve *A*, to the condenser-liquid receiver, where it absorbs the heat of condensation from the refrigerant. From the condenser-liquid receiver the water passes through valve *D* to the drain. Pump 1 circulates the cooling water through the conditioner coil where it absorbs heat from the air going to the conditioned space. From the conditioner coil the water passes through valve *B* to the cooler where it is reduced in temperature by the refrigerant. From

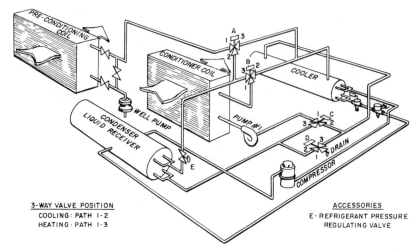

3-WAY VALVE POSITION
COOLING: PATH 1-2
HEATING: PATH 1-3

ACCESSORIES
E- REFRIGERANT PRESSURE
REGULATING VALVE

Figure 3-7   Water as a heat source-sink and water as heating and cooling medium (fixed refrigerant circuit—water flow reversed).

the cooler the cold water passes through valve C to the pump, to repeat the cycle.

During the heating cycle the three-way valves are positioned to path 1–3. The well pump circulates the water through the preconditioning coil to preheat the ventilation air. The heat source water then circulates through valve A to the cooler, where heat is absorbed by the refrigerant. From the cooler the water passes through valve D to the drain. Pump 1 circulates the warm water through the conditioner coil, where it gives up the heat to the air going to the conditioned space. From the conditioner coil the water passes through valve B to the condenser-liquid receiver, where it absorbs heat of condensation from the refrigerant gas. From the condenser-liquid receiver, the water passes through valve C, to repeat the cycle.

In the water-to-water design, water is used as the heat source-sink and water is used to transfer heat from the condenser and cooler. The refrigerant flow is always in the same direction, going from the compressor to condenser, where the refrigerant is liquefied by giving up its latent heat of condensation to the circulating water. From the condenser the liquid refrigerant flows through the expansion valve to the cooler, where it changes into a gas and absorbs the heat of vaporization by reducing the temperature of the circulating water. From the cooler the low-temperature refrigerant gas returns to the compressor.

Refrigerant pressure regulating valve E, in the entering water line to the condenser-liquid receiver, regulates the water flow to maintain a predetermined refrigerant condensing pressure.

SIMULTANEOUS HEATING AND COOLING AND HEAT RECLAIMING CYCLE

The performance of any year-round air conditioning system will be influenced by a number of design and application factors such as the architectural aspects of the structure, geographic location, the outdoor temperature, cycle and operating characteristics of the equipment, economizers and other heat recovery devices, method of operating the system, and the amount of ventilation air used during both the occupied and unoccupied periods.

The orientation and relative amounts of perimeter and internal areas now being used in the modern office buildings, department stores, and commercial structures, together with accompanying internal heat gains from lights, people, and heat producing equipment are major influencing factors in the proper selection of air conditioning systems. To provide indoor comfort, the air conditioning system may be called upon simultaneously to furnish heating to the exterior zones and cooling to the interior, even on the coldest winter day.

The heat pump, because of its many inherent design features, is readily adaptable to such applications. In many instances the cooling effect supplied to the internal areas by the heat pump can be made to serve as the heat source for the heat delivered to the exterior areas. Also, reheat can be furnished at the same time to maintain a closer control of relative humidity. In contrast, it is often necessary with other types of air conditioning systems to reject the condenser heat to the outside when cooling is required in the internal areas, and to provide heat from another source for the reheat cycle and for the perimeter areas. This latter method of heating and cooling can add considerably to the operating cost.

WATER AS THE HEAT SOURCE-SINK WITH FIXED REFRIGERANT CIRCUIT FOR SIMULTANEOUS HEATING AND COOLING

Water is used as the heat source-sink and as the medium to provide simultaneous heating and cooling to the conditioned space. In this arrangement the refrigerant flow is always in the same direction, going from the compressor to the condenser, then to the cooler. The major refrigerant components together with all refrigerant piping and accessories can be purchased as a compact package with a hermetically sealed refrigerant circuit. The hot and cold water piping, the indirect heating and cooling surfaces, and other needed accessories for a particular installation can, in turn, be installed by the contractor.

During a considerable portion of the year the heating and cooling requirements of the structure may be in balance, so that an external heat source or sink is not required. Thus, the heat removed from the zones requiring cooling is automatically transferred to the condenser circuit and made available to the zones requiring heat. In this way the coefficient of performance is materially improved to give a considerable saving in operating cost.

Figure 3-8 illustrates how simultaneous heating and cooling are readily available at all times. For the basic heating cycle, valves are

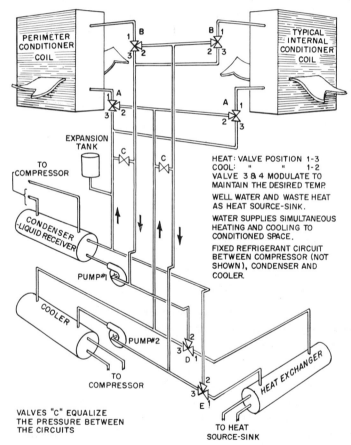

Figure 3-8 Water as heat source-sink and water as the medium to provide simultaneous heating and cooling (fixed refrigerant circuit—water flow reversed).

positioned to path 1–3 to provide two water circuits. Pump 1 circulates the warm water through the condenser-liquid receiver, valves A, the conditioner coils, and valves B in a closed loop. Pump 2 circulates the cold water through the cooler, valve D, the exchanger (where heat is taken from the well water), and valve E back to pump 2 to repeat the cycle.

For the basic cooling cycle, valves are positioned to path 1–2. Pump 1 circulates the warm water through the condenser, valve E, the exchanger (where heat is rejected to the well water), and valve D back to pump 1. Pump 2 circulates the cold water through the cooler (where heat is taken from the water by the refrigerant), valves A, the conditioner coil, and valves B back to pump 2 in a closed loop.

During the intermediate cycle, simultaneous heating and cooling are provided by modulating valves D and E to maintain the desired temperatures in the two circuits. Usually, during this cycle, the water is maintained at 100 to 120 F in the condenser circuit and 45 to 50 F in the chiller circuit. The excess heating and cooling are rejected from the exchanger to the well water. The well water can be supplied directly to the condenser and chiller circuits instead of through the heat exchanger, as indicated. The direct use of the well water is most attractive, provided it is chemically acceptable and does not unduly contaminate the heat transfer surfaces.

The compressor (not shown) delivers the hot compressed gas to the condenser-liquid receiver where it is liquefied, giving up its latent heat of condensation to the circulating water. From the condenser the liquid refrigerant flows through an expansion valve to the cooler (where it changes into a gas), absorbing the heat of vaporization by reducing the temperature of the circulating water, and then returns to the compressor.

AIR AS THE HEAT SOURCE-SINK WITH FIXED REFRIGERANT CIRCUIT FOR SIMULTANEOUS HEATING AND COOLING

Figure 3-9 shows the flow diagram of an air heat source-sink design employing a liquid as the transfer medium between the refrigerant and the transfer surfaces. The operation of this system is identical to that for the well water cycle illustrated in Figure 3-8 except that outdoor air instead of well water is the heat source and sink. In areas where below-freezing outdoor temperatures are experienced, an antifreeze solution such as inhibited ethylene glycol and water solution must be used in the cooler circuit.

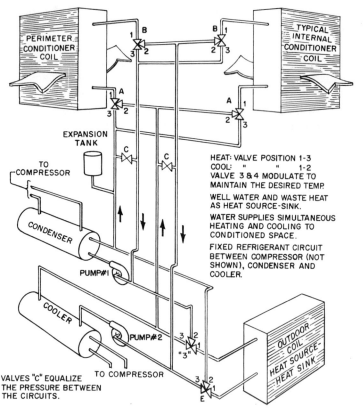

Figure 3-9   Air as a heat source-sink and an intermediate liquid as the medium to provide simultaneous heating and cooling (fixed refrigerant circuit).

AIR AS HEAT SOURCE-SINK AND AIR AS HEATING AND COOLING MEDIUM (*Changing Direction of Refrigerant Flow for Simultaneous Heating and Cooling*)

Figure 3-10 shows a simultaneous heating and cooling cycle which operates by changing the direction of the refrigerant. Air is used as the heat source and sink and air as the heating and cooling to the conditioned space. This same cycle can also be employed with water as the heat source-sink and water as the heating and cooling medium going to the conditioned space.

The heat removed from the areas requiring cooling may be transferred to the zones needing heating in a manner similar to that described for the indirect systems. One major advantage of this system over the indirect method is the elimination of the additional heat transfer surfaces. This advantage may be offset in some instances by the precautions which must be observed to assure proper refrigerant flow and the desired capacity modulation. Each installation, however, must be evaluated to determine which cycle is the most practical and, at the same time, gives the most satisfactory performance. Such an analysis is particularly necessary for multizone installations where the heat source-sink equipment must be located a considerable distance from the compressors.

During the basic heating cycle valves 1, 3, and 4 are open. The compressor delivers the hot compressed refrigerant gas through valve 1 to the heating surface (where it is condensed), giving up its latent heat of condensation to the air going to the conditioned space. From the heating coil the liquid refrigerant flows to the liquid receiver and then through valve 4 and the expansion valve to the outdoor coil. In the outdoor coil the liquid refrigerant changes into a gas, absorbing the heat of vaporization from the outdoor air. From the outdoor coil the refrigerant gas returns through valve 3 to the compressor to repeat the cycle.

During the basic cooling cycle valves 2 and 5 are open. The compressor delivers the hot compressed refrigerant through valve 2 to the outdoor coil (where it is condensed), giving up its latent heat of condensation to the outside air. From the outside coil the liquid re-

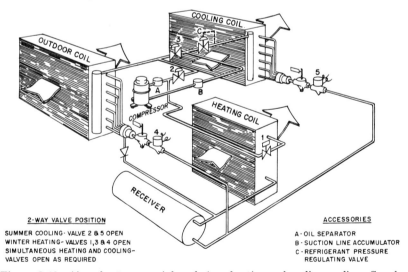

2-WAY VALVE POSITION

SUMMER COOLING- VALVE 2 & 5 OPEN
WINTER HEATING- VALVES 1,3 & 4 OPEN
SIMULTANEOUS HEATING AND COOLING-
VALVES OPEN AS REQUIRED

ACCESSORIES

A - OIL SEPARATOR
B - SUCTION LINE ACCUMULATOR
C - REFRIGERANT PRESSURE
     REGULATING VALVE

Figure 3-10 Air as heat source-sink and air as heating and cooling medium. Supplemental heating coil to provide simultaneous heating and cooling by changing direction of refrigerant flow.

frigerant flows through the check valve, the liquid receiver, valve 5, and the expansion valve to the cooling coil. At the cooling surface the liquid is changed into a gas by absorbing the heat of vaporization from the air going to the conditioned space. From the cooling coil the refrigerant gas returns to the compressor through suction throttling valve C to repeat the cycle.

During the intermediate cycle, when the outdoor coil is being used as a heat source, valves 1, 3, 4, and 5 are open to provide simultaneous heating and cooling as required. When the outdoor coil is being used as a heat sink valves 2 and 5 remain open to provide the cooling and 1 is open, as required, to provide simultaneous heating.

AUXILIARY COIL FOR SIMULTANEOUS HEATING AND COOLING

An auxiliary coil can be easily added to the various designs if supplemental heating and/or cooling is required. One method of incorporating an auxiliary coil in the basic air heat source-sink cycle is shown in Figure 3-11. When the system is on the basic heating cycle the auxiliary coil furnishes supplemental cooling while the conditioner coil furnishes the heating. Conversely, when the system is on the cooling cycle the auxiliary coil will furnish supplemental heating while the conditioner coil furnishes the required cooling.

This particular design is not so flexible nor is its operating

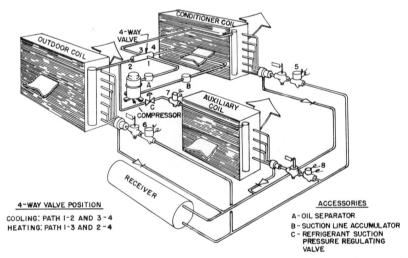

4-WAY VALVE POSITION

COOLING: PATH 1-2 AND 3-4
HEATING: PATH 1-3 AND 2-4

ACCESSORIES

A - OIL SEPARATOR
B - SUCTION LINE ACCUMULATOR
C - REFRIGERANT SUCTION
      PRESSURE REGULATING
      VALVE

Figure 3-11 Air as heat source-sink and air as heating and cooling medium. Auxiliary coil for simultaneous heating and cooling. Throttling valves used to regulate refrigerant effect.

efficiency so high as in the other, simultaneous heating and cooling systems. It may be advantageous, however, if the supplemental heating or cooling requirements coincide with the base load operation. Since the auxiliary coil is in parallel to the outdoor heat source-sink coil, it must necessarily be exposed to the same refrigerant temperature and pressure. Therefore, no gain in efficiency is obtained by using the supplemental coil.

The position of the four-way valve in this cycle is the same as described in connection with Figure 3-1. The additional valves 7 and 8 are used to obtain the required simultaneous heating and cooling for the auxiliary coil and to take the coil out of service during the defrost cycle.

STORAGE SYSTEM FOR HEATING AND COOLING, WITH REFRIGERANT FLOW REVERSED (*Fixed Air and Water Circuits*)

The air-to-water design (Figure 3-3) uses air as the heat source and water as the transfer medium between the air going to the conditioned space and the refrigerant circulating through the condenser-cooler. This design is readily adaptable to a storage system, as shown in Figure 3-12.

With such an arrangement it is possible, when on the heating cycle, to store hot water during mild weather for use when lower outdoor temperatures are experienced and, when on the cooling cycle, to store the cold water during mild weather for use when higher outdoor temperatures are experienced. It is also possible to

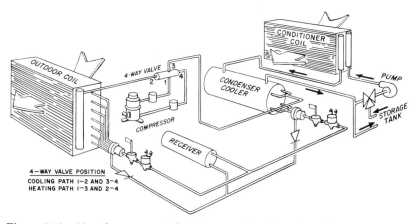

Figure 3-12 Air as heat source-sink and water as heating and cooling medium—using storage tank (fixed water and air circuits—refrigerant flow reversed).

store either hot or cold water, depending on the cycle of operation, during the night or off-peak periods for use during the day or when the demand is greatest. For cooling, the refrigerant path leads from the compressor through the four-way valve, path 1–2, the outdoor air coil, the check valve, the liquid receiver, the expansion valve, the condenser-cooler, and the four-way valve, path 3–4, back to the compressor to repeat the cycle. For heating, the refrigerant goes from the compressor through the four-way valve, path 1–3, the condenser-cooler, the check valve, the liquid receiver, the expansion valve, the outdoor coil, and the four-way valve, path 2–4, back to the compressor to repeat the cycle.

During both the cooling and the heating cycles the pump circulates water in a closed loop through the conditioner coil, the condenser-cooler, and/or the storage tank, depending on the position of the three-way valve.

STORAGE SYSTEM FOR HEATING AND COOLING, WITH FIXED REFRIGERANT FLOW (*Water Flow Reversed*)

Another possible simultaneous heating and cooling system with storage is illustrated in Figure 3-13. This cycle is similar to the simultaneous heating and cooling cycle as shown in Figures 3-8 and 3-9 except that the structure heat gain instead of outdoor air and well water is used as a heat source. Such a cycle is particularly advantageous when considerable internal excess heat can be reclaimed as a supplement for the perimeter zones on extremely cold winter days and when little or no heat from an outside source is required to maintain comfort during the occupied hours. In this design the excess heat from the internal zone (over that required by the perimeter zones) may be stored in the tank for future use as a supplemental heat when the structure heat loss exceeds that available as internal heat gain. Such a storage arrangement has the further advantage of permitting off-peak direct electric heating and off-peak cooling during the summer period, in order to take full advantage of the lower electric energy cost which is available from many utilities.

The condenser shown in Figure 3-13 has two separate water circuits, one for the outdoor heat sink and the other for the indoor conditioners. In this way atmospheric pollution or other such impurities are not transferred to the indoor circuits and at the same time the design problems caused by the difference in pressure between the two circuits are eliminated.

Heating is provided to the perimeter conditioner coils by positioning valves A–1 and B–1 to path 1–3. Pump 1 circulates the warm

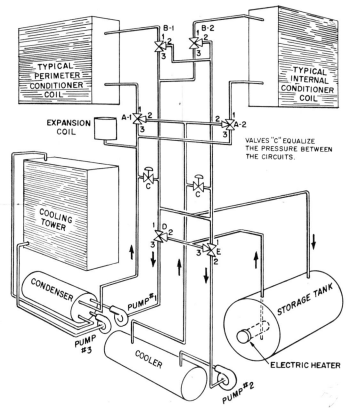

Figure 3-13 System employing storage tank and using waste heat as heat source and cooling tower as heat sink. Water is used to supply simultaneous heating and cooling to conditioned space. Fixed refrigerant circuit between compressor (not shown), condenser, and cooler.

water, in a closed loop, through the condenser, valve A–1, the perimeter conditioner coils, valve B–1, and valve D. The modulating valve D between the closed loop and the storage tank maintains a predetermined water temperature, generally between 100 to 120 F in the condenser circuit.

As the water temperature rises in the condenser circuit, valve D diverts the warmer water to the top of the storage tank and takes the cooler make-up water from the bottom of the tank. When the storage tank is fully charged with hot water, condenser pump 3 is operated to dissipate the excess heat to the cooling tower or some other heat sink. During periods when the reclaimed heat from the internal areas is insufficient to maintain the desired condenser water temperature, modulating valve D is also positioned to use warmer water from the storage tank.

Simultaneous cooling is provided to the internal conditioner coil by positioning valves A–2 and B–2 to path 1–2. Pump 2 circulates the cold water through the cooler, valve A–2, the internal conditioner coils, valve B–2 and valve E. The modulating valve E maintains a predetermined water temperature in the range of 45 to 55 F in the cooler circuit. When the temperature of the water in the storage tank is reduced below a level that is no longer suitable for direct heating, the modulating valve E can be positioned to use this water as a heat source down to a temperature of about 40 to 45 F. In this way a considerable amount of additional heat can be recovered from the storage tank to improve the overall system efficiency. The same operating cycle can also be used to provide off-peak cold water storage during summer periods.

If a good heat balance between the internal and perimeter areas is not obtained this type of storage may not be applicable or acceptable. It may be that supplemental resistance heat will be practical to heat the storage tank water for the short, infrequent periods (mostly during the nights or weekends) when maximum benefit is obtained from the lower electrical rates. Another possible alternative, previously mentioned, is to introduce an outside heat source into the circuit, as illustrated by Figures 3-8 and 3-9. In this arrangement the water storage tank could be in parallel with the internal conditioner coil.

REFERENCES

Arnold, Richard S., When, Where, What to Specify in Heat Pumps, *Actual Specifying Engineer,* September 1958.

ASHRAE Guide and Data Book (1964), Applications, Chap. 6, Heat Pump Systems for Air Conditioning, American Society of Heating, Ventilating and Air Conditioning.

Harnish, J. R., Achieving Economy in the Design and Use of Heat Pumps, *Air Conditioning, Heating and Ventilating,* August 1959.

Rex, Harland E., Refrigerating Equipment for the Citrus Industry, *Refrigerating Engineering,* 43 (November 1957).

Chapter 4

Equipment Selection and Application

The design and application practices for compressors, heat transfer surfaces, and associated components which are normally followed in comfort cooling installations are adequately covered by air conditioning text books and manufacturers' product manuals. Consequently, this chapter is limited to those equipment selection and application aspects which are essential for the practical and satisfactory operation of heat pumps.

A logical first step in designing a heat pump installation is to choose the heat source and sink and then to select the basic type of system to be employed, as explained in Chapters 2 and 3. The required heating and cooling capacity of the system at design temperatures must then be determined in order to size the compressor and the heat transfer surfaces properly.

HEATING AND COOLING LOAD DETERMINATION

The heating and cooling requirements of a structure at design conditions must be calculated in accordance with the latest recommended procedures of the recognized heating, air conditioning, and refrigeration societies. It is necessary to determine with accuracy the design cooling load as well as the heating load. This is important because the heat pump equipment is normally sized for the cooling load. In this case the resulting heating output, if inadequate, can be supplemented by resistance heaters to satisfy the design heating requirements. It is uneconomical, with few exceptions, to purposely oversize the cooling equipment to obtain the heating output at design conditions.

Consideration must be given to the required capacities and operating cycles at other than design conditions. In many instances it will be necessary to investigate the necessity of using the cooling coils and the condensers to provide simultaneous heating and cooling. It has been found that a high percentage of internal heat gain in commercial or industrial establishments can contribute to the heating requirements of the structure. Such useful heat gain includes sensible heat from the people, heat dissipated by the lights, computers, fans, and other electrical or mechanical equipment. Some judgement must be exercised as to the amount of internal heat gain which can be safely considered as useful during the heating cycle. Methods for effectively using these internal heat gains, particularly during the heating cycle, are more thoroughly described in Chapter 5 in connection with the description of combined lighting and air conditioning systems. In order to size the cooling equipment properly, it is equally important to determine the amount of internal heat gain which will coincide with the other design cooling loads during the summer. For instance, 100 percent of the heat from the lights may be advantageously used during the heating cycle, but frequently a lower percentage, such as 75 percent can be considered as a safe coincident demand to the other loads during the cooling cycle.

It is good practice to base the structure's ventilation requirements during the occupied periods on the latest authoritative recommendations. During the unoccupied periods, however, the ventilation quantities should be equal to the natural infiltration rate of the structure. Consequently, it is most essential to make heat loss and heat gain calculations for each of these two conditions in order to evaluate correctly the effect of the internal heat gain on the equipment selection and the annual operating cost.

It is very important to have a practical balance between the design heating and cooling requirements. Therefore, as recommended in Chapter 6, full utilization should be made of all heat conservation devices, such as wall and roof thermal insulation, double windows, electric-carbon filters (to permit minimum ventilation air usage), and heat exchangers to recover heat from the exhaust air.

No practical method has been accepted by the air conditioning industry for estimating the useful solar heat gain in a building during the heating cycle. It is known, however, that the heating requirements of a structure can be materially reduced if effective use is made of the available solar energy. Several possibilities for using solar energy to improve the heat pump performance is discussed in Chapter 2.

COMPRESSOR PERFORMANCE

The type of compressor and the refrigerant employed to get maximum economy depend to a large extent on the capacity required and the working pressures needed to satisfy the design conditions. Refrigeration compressors are either of the balanced-compression or free-compression type. With balanced compression the necessary positive displacement is generally obtained by either a reciprocating or a rotary mechanism. With free compression a turbo-type or a jet-type compressor is employed. A turbo compressor, whether of the centrifugal or axial flow construction, is primarily suited to those services where large volumes of fluid must be handled. The jet compressor is similarly suited for large fluid volumes and low compression ratios. The positive displacement compressor, on the other hand, is best suited for handling smaller volumes of gases with larger compression ratios. Reciprocating compressors, therefore, are generally selected for all air heat source-sink systems and for the small and the medium-sized water heat source-sink units. Centrifugal compressors are generally used for the larger water heat source-sink systems and for the heat reclaiming cycles discussed in Chapter 3.

Typical performance curves of a reciprocating compressor at various saturated suction refrigerant temperatures and outdoor temperatures during both the heating and the cooling cycles are given in Figure 4-1. This compressor has a 100-ton cooling capacity at a 95 F outdoor temperature and a 40 F saturated suction temperature. It can be seen that during the heating cycle both the refrigerating effect and the corresponding heating output from the condenser reduce proportionally to the drop in outdoor temperature. Similarly, during the cooling cycle the cooling capacity and the corresponding condenser output are also reduced as the outdoor temperature increases. This adverse operating condition is frequently cited as the main disadvantage of an air heat source-sink heat pump. The importance of liquid subcooling on the heating output is shown by the upper curve of Figure 4-1. Several other ways of improving the performance at the extreme outdoor temperatures are also given in this chapter.

For comparative purposes, typical performance curves of a typical unitary heat pump with a 4-ton cooling capacity are given in Figure 4-2 for various outdoor temperatures. It can be noted that a similar relationship exists between the heating and cooling capacities and the outdoor temperatures for the two sizes that represent a wide range in tonnage. It can be noted that an average heating

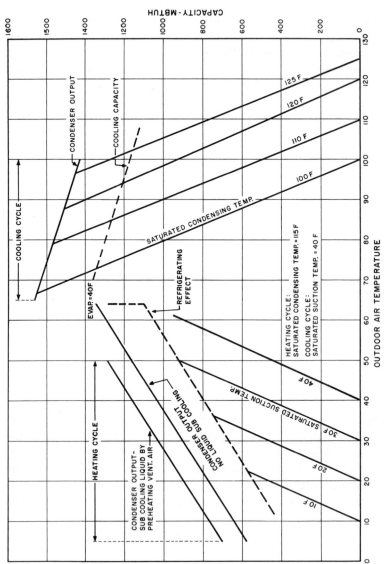

Figure 4-1 Heating capacities at various outdoor air and saturated refrigerant temperatures for heat pump having a 100-ton cooling capacity.

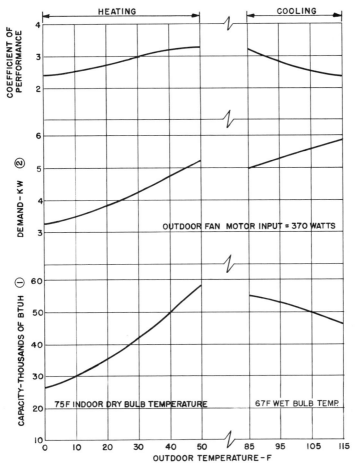

Figure 4-2 Performance characteristics using air as the heat source and heat sink. Typical 4-ton heat pump.

coefficient of performance (based on compressor and outdoor fan kilowatts) of 3 is given for the 4-ton unit at an outdoor temperature of 30 F. A higher coefficient of performance, over the entire outdoor temperature range, can be obtained with some types of equipment, and this improvement will become more prevalent as the manufacturers employ more efficient combinations of equipment and operating cycles. This is particularly true for the larger equipment because of a greater freedom in the selection of the components and because of the possibility of effectively using the liquid subcooling effect. The

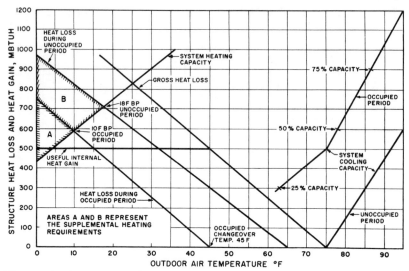

Figure 4-3 Structure heat loss and heat gain at various outdoor temperatures, compared with heat pump having a 100-ton cooling capacity.

heating and cooling capacity, kilowatt input, coefficient of performance, and other needed data for plotting Figures 4-1 and 4-2 can usually be obtained from manufacturers' published data.

The gross and the net heating requirements of the structure can be superimposed on the heat pump capacity curves, as shown in Figure 4-3, to obtain the respective balance points. The most practical compressor selection is obtained by sizing the equipment for the cooling load and by supplementing any deficiency in the heating requirements with electric resistance heat, or by a multi-staging of the compressors. In the figure, the balance point varies from 10 F to 25 F, depending on the temperature and method of operation. The required supplemental heating is given by area *A* for the occupied period and by areas *A* plus *B* during the unoccupied period. Comparative curves, as shown by curves 4–1, 4–2, and 4–3, are very useful for investigating the advisability of reducing the heating or cooling loads, for checking the requirements of the heat source or sink at various operating conditions, or for determining the characteristics of the required control system. Such comparative curves are also very valuable for estimating the energy requirements and operating cost.

It is interesting to note, in connection with Figure 4-1, that a heat pump system having a 100-ton cooling capacity and using a 55 F constant water temperature as the heat source (to give approximately a 40 F suction saturated refrigerant temperature) would deliver about 1400 MBtuh during the heating cycle. This capacity could easily furnish the heating requirements at all conditions for the example illustrated in Figure 4-3, without supplemental heating. This is usually the case with a water source heat pump and represents one of its main advantages over an air heat source system. Unfortunately, chemically suited well water is becoming increasingly difficult to find in many areas, as explained in Chapter 2. Also, in many cases, disposal of the water is a problem and the cost of drilling the well and maintaining the pump further detracts from its use. It is for these reasons that heat pumps using outdoor air as the heat source and sink are receiving favorable consideration in many areas and, with all factors considered, usually prove to be the most practical and satisfactory heat source.

MULTI-STAGED COMPRESSORS

The majority of air source heat pump installations employ single-stage reciprocating machines, but multi-stage compression systems have been used to a limited extent. These two-stage systems could be attractive for the large commercial and industrial installations in northern climates where the low temperatures may make the single-stage system impractical.

In the two-stage arrangement, the compressors are used in parallel during the cooling cycle and in parallel or series during the heating cycle, as shown in Figure 4-4. During the heating cycle the

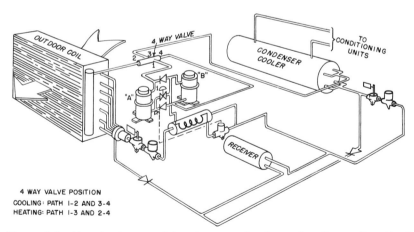

4 WAY VALVE POSITION
COOLING: PATH 1-2 AND 3-4
HEATING: PATH 1-3 AND 2-4

Figure 4-4 Air as heat source-sink and water as heating and cooling medium (fixed air and water circuits—refrigerant flow reversed). With series-parallel compressor arrangement to provide two-stage compression at low outdoor air temperatures. Compressor "A": single-stage cooling—high-stage heating; Compressor "B": single-stage cooling—low-stage heating; valve 1 opened to provide two-stage operation.

system operates on single stage with compressor B, or can switch to multi-stage compression at the lower outdoor temperatures. For the multi-stage cycle, valve 1 is energized and the high-temperature, high-pressure refrigerant gas from compressor B is discharged into the suction intake of compressor A, where it is raised to a still higher temperature and pressure. From compressor A the gas is delivered through a four-way valve, path 1–3 to the condenser-cooler where it condenses and gives up its latent heat of condensation to heat the water going to the conditioning units. The discharged gas temperature from compressor B is reduced to an acceptable level before entering the compressor A by means of the indicated refrigerant intercooler.

The main advantage of compressor staging is to obtain increased heating output at the lower outdoor temperature, as shown in Figure 4-5. Other advantages can be the resultant smaller heat source-sink surface and other auxiliaries, which may accrue from the use of a larger air-refrigerant temperature difference.

As indicated in Figure 4-5, the performance of the two-stage and

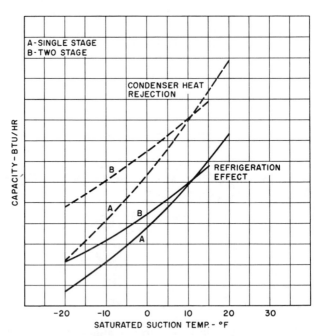

Figure 4-5 Comparative curves of condenser heat rejection and refrigeration effect at various saturated suction temperatures for single-stage and two-stage operation (F12 refrigerant). (Carrier Air Conditioning Co.)

the single-stage compressor are about the same at a suction temperature of 10 F, which is equivalent to an outdoor temperature of 20 to 25 F. Above this temperature the single stage is more efficient and below this point the two stage usually has the advantage in heat delivered per kilowatt input. Whether this increased heating effect will outweigh the disadvantage of the higher first cost of staging will depend upon the design, application requirement, and geographic location of a particular installation.

COOLING AND HEATING SURFACES

The indoor and outdoor coils are sized and selected in accordance with the accepted refrigeration and air conditioning practice. It is essential that the heat-transfer surfaces be selected to operate at relatively small air-refrigerant temperature differences (oftentimes 6 to 10 F) in order to maintain the lowest possible condensing temperature and the highest suction temperature. A change in the mean effective temperature difference between the surface and the heat source of 2 or 3 F, as an example, can result in a 20 to 50 percent difference in the output of the unit or in the amount of required surface. Rule of thumb method, unfounded assumptions, or pyramiding of safety factors are discouraged because they can increase the cost of the system beyond the point of practicality or else result in an unacceptable, low performance factor with a corresponding high operating cost.

When air is used as the heat source, an effort should be made to obtain an outdoor coil, air flow combination which will have the lowest first cost and at the same time have the highest coefficient of performance (cp). Figure 4-6 illustrates how the useful heating effect and coefficient of performance vary with air flow over the outdoor coil during the heating cycle. It can be noticed from this figure that above a certain air flow, the cp decreases and the useful heat increases as the air flow over the outdoor coil increases. The objective, therefore, is to select the air flow to give the highest cp and still obtain the desired performance. Quite often it may be found necessary to select the air flow slightly above the point where the maximum heating cp would be obtained, in order to prevent excessive compressor head pressures during the cooling cycle.

Sometimes water sprays are employed to increase the heat sink capacity of the outdoor coils rather than increase the air quantity, when summer cooling is the controlling design requirement. When all things are considered, however, the straight air coil is preferred. In the most recent designs multi-propeller fans are used instead of

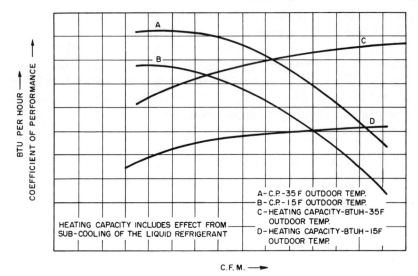

Figure 4-6 Relationship between heating capacity, coefficient of performance (cp) of the heat pump system and various air flows over the outdoor coils. (Sporn, Ambrose, *ASHVE Transactions,* **57,** 1951.)

a single large blower which permits using variable outdoor air quantities quite easily and economically to obtain the maximum coefficient of performance under all operating conditions.

The same procedure used for selecting the outdoor air surface is followed in obtaining a suitable condenser-cooler combination when using water as the heat source and sink. The necessary pumping depth of the well, the available water quantity, the water temperature, and the heating and cooling requirements are all important and influencial factors which must be considered to obtain the most practical selection with the highest possible coefficient of performance.

REFRIGERANT PIPING

Refrigerant piping between the various equipment should be properly sized and installed in accordance with the accepted refrigeration practices given in any good air conditioning and refrigeration manual or textbook.

As in all mechanical refrigeration systems, care is necessary in sizing and installing the refrigerant piping to minimize liquid refrigerant floodback and to assure proper oil return, particularly if some form of capacity modulation is installed or if multiple compressors are used.

In a number of the basic designs given in Chapter 3 the direct expansion type of indoor and outdoor heat transfer surfaces serve both as condensers and evaporators. Because of this dual duty, these surfaces must have refrigerant headers to provide good distribution when serving as evaporators and proper drainage when serving as condensers.

SUCTION LINE ACCUMULATORS

Good practice, in both the small and the large commercial and industrial installations, is to employ a suction line accumulator similar to that shown in Figure 4-7, as further protection against migration and harmful liquid floodback to the compressor.

There are a number of different possible accumulator designs. The objective is to retard the liquid flow through the accumulator B by a sudden decrease in velocity and/or by means of a series of baffles and filters. In some designs the liquid refrigerant is passed through a heat exchanger coil, located at the bottom of the accumulator, to superheat the liquid-oil mixture. In the larger, central station type of installation a valve, adjusted to an acceptable bleed rate, can be provided to allow the collected liquid and oil in the accumulator to return slowly to the compressor through the solenoid valve, strainer, throttling valve circuit, as illustrated in the circled portion of the figure. The solenoid valve in this circuit is closed when the compressor is not operating to prevent gravity flow during the shutdown periods. On the larger systems, also, a similar accumulator or separator A can be used in the compressor discharge line to serve as

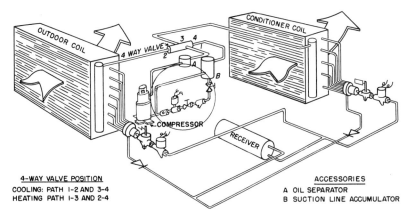

4-WAY VALVE POSITION
COOLING: PATH 1-2 AND 3-4
HEATING PATH 1-3 AND 2-4

ACCESSORIES
A OIL SEPARATOR
B SUCTION LINE ACCUMULATOR

Figure 4-7 Air as heat source-sink and air as heating and cooling medium (fixed air circuits—refrigerant flow reversed). Expansion valves used to regulate refrigerant effect.

a sonic filter and to reduce oil entrainment through the refrigerant circuit. The collected oil in the discharge line separator is returned through a float switch to the compressor crankcase.

LIQUID SUBCOOLING COILS

The use of a refrigerant subcooling coil to preheat the ventilation air during the heating cycle is a practical and efficient way of materially increasing the heating output and performance factor of many types of systems employing reasonably large quantities of ventilation air. In many instances a liquid subcooling coil can be added to the heat pump cycle between the liquid receiver and the heat source surface as illustrated in Figure 4-8. During the heating cycle the warm liquid refrigerant from the liquid receiver flows through the subcooling coil to preheat the ventilation air and at the same time lower the temperature of the refrigerant. Lowering the refrigerant temperature in this manner materially increases the refrigerant effect per pound of refrigerant circulated, as illustrated by enthalpy diagram 1-5 in Chapter 1, to improve the efficiency of the cycle. At the same time, the heating capacity can be increased as much as 20 percent, as indicated in Figure 4-9 (with a proportional increase in the performance factor), depending upon the refrigerant circulating rate and other influencing factors. The attractiveness of the arrangement, as Figure 4-9 shows, is that the capacity

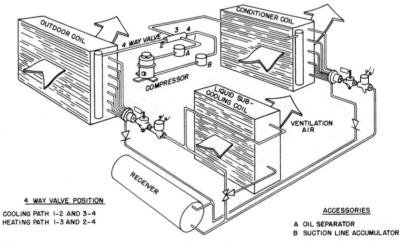

Figure 4-8 Air as heat source-sink and air as heating and cooling medium. Supplemental liquid subcooling coil in ventilation air supply to increase heating effect and to improve coefficient of performance during heating cycle.

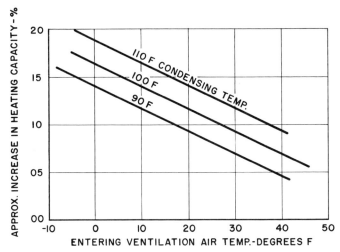

Figure 4-9   Expected increase in the heating capacity resulting from the effective preheating of the ventilation air by subcooling the liquid refrigerant. (Carrier Air Conditioning Co.)

increase is greatest during the colder outdoor temperatures when the maximum heat losses are being experienced. The subcooling coil must be properly located in the cycle so that the heat from the liquid is rejected to the outdoor air heat source coil instead of preheating the ventilation air during the cooling cycle.

Similarly, when well water is being used as the heat source-sink (as illustrated in Figure 3-7 of Chapter 3), a well water coil can be installed between the well pump and the condenser-cooler to preheat the ventilation air in the winter and precool it in the summer. This supplemental surface materially increases the heating and cooling capacity and the performance factor of the system. Counterflow of the well water and outdoor air is used to obtain maximum effect. With this arrangement it is possible to preheat the ventilation air 40 to 50 F during the cold winter months and precool it 25 to 35 F during the summer months, depending upon the well water circulation rate and upon the quantity and temperature of the ventilation air. Caution must be exercised against freezing the water in the coil. As long as the correct amount of water is flowing properly through the coil, there is little danger of freezing, since the initial 50 to 60 F well water is reduced only 2 or 3 F under normal operation. The water may freeze in the coil when exposed to ventilation air temperature below 32 F if something happens to interfere with the proper flow pattern. Figure 4-10 shows one of several ways of preventing coil

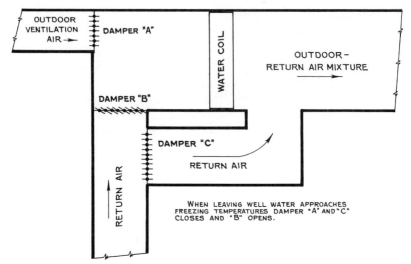

Figure 4-10   Location of dampers in outdoor and return air circuit to help prevent freezing of the water coil.

damage in case the water temperature approaches the freezing point. An immersion safety thermostat, set at about 40 F and located preferably in the leaving water coil header, could position the outdoor recirculated air volume dampers A, B, and C to reduce the outdoor ventilation air and cause the warmer return air from the space to pass over the water coil. An immersion safety thermostat could also sound an alarm or energize a signal to warn of the impending danger.

FROSTING AND DEFROSTING OF HEAT SOURCE COILS

Frost will occur on the heat-absorbing surface of an air source heat pump when low-temperature and high-humidity air prevails for long periods of time. This frost accumulation is a result of moisture condensing and freezing as the air is cooled below the dewpoint by contact with a surface at a temperature of 32 F or lower.

Heavy defrost deposits adversely affect the efficiency of the refrigeration system. Frost accumulation of up to 2 or 3 lb per sq ft of coil surface has not been found seriously to impair the transfer rate between the refrigerant surface and air. Beyond this point, however, the surfaces must be periodically defrosted to maintain good heat transfer and thus prevent the compressor from operating at a lower suction pressure, with a corresponding reduction in the heating capacity and coefficient of performance.

The outdoor fans are made inoperative during the defrost cycle to minimize the heat loss to the atmosphere. Provisions are also generally made to heat the drain pan, sometimes used below the outdoor coil, in order to melt pieces of ice or to prevent refreezing the water falling from the coil during defrost. This heater may consist of small tubing fastened to the bottom of the drain pan, through which the hot refrigerant gas passes on the way to the condenser. The more common application, however, employs small electric resistance tubular heaters fastened to the bottom of the drain pan. In addition, drain lines from the pan must be of the correct size and well pitched to carry away the water and must also be wrapped with a heating cable which, in turn, is thermally insulated to keep the line warm at all times.

Frequency of Defrost Cycle. The frequency of defrosting will be influenced by a number of factors, including outdoor temperatures, relative humidities, coil design, and hours of operation. The ability of the air to hold water vapor is adversely proportional to the outdoor temperature. Consequently, at the colder temperature, the total precipitation on the surface and the eventual frost formation will be less per pound of dry air circulated. At 20 F and 60 percent relative humidity (10 F dew point), for example, frequent defrosting is not required. From this low point the number of daily defrosts increases, with higher outdoor temperatures and humidities until a 32 F dew point temperature is reached. Above 32 F dew point the defrost cycle decreases until at about 52 F DB no frost at all occurs on the coils. Moisture in the air may still condense at these higher temperatures, but does not freeze because the refrigerant surface temperature is above 32 F.

The variation in the frequency of the defrost cycle is illustrated by Figure 4-11 which shows the average number of defrost cycles, in a 24-hour period, at various dry bulb and dew point temperatures for a typical, small unitary heat pump. It is indicated that two defrosts for each 24-hr period can be expected at a 10 F dew point, which can be simulated by 20 F DB and 60 percent RH, and 22 defrosts can result at a 27 F dew point, which is equivalent to a 30 F DB and 90 percent RH.

Unfortunately, dewpoint temperatures and their respective hours of occurrence, together with resulting temperatures of the heat source surfaces, are not readily available for most areas. Some idea of the number of defrost cycles for a given period may be obtained in many instances by referring to climatological data, similar to those given by Table 9-1 or Figures 9-3, 9-5 of Chapter 9.

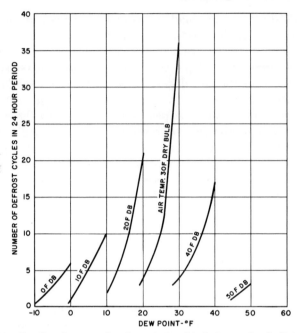

Figure 4-11   Family of curves showing relationship between dry bulb temperature, dew point temperature, and no. of defrost cycles in 24-hour period to maintain satisfactory operation.

It can be noted from these data, for this particular region, that about 900 hr of below-freezing temperature occur during a normal season, with a weighted average temperature of 28 F. In all probability the average relative humidity below 32 F would not exceed 80 percent to give a dew point of 23 F (28 F DB and 80 percent RH). Figure 4-11 shows that under such conditions ten defrosts can be expected in a 24-hr period to give about 360 defrost cycles on an annual basis.

The number of defrost cycles could easily range from 100 to 500 during a season, depending on the design and control of the heat pump equipment. The maximum defrost recorded during a 24-hr period was 40, which occurred during a freezing rain condition at an outdoor temperature of 33 F and 100 percent RH.

Defrosting Cycles

Hot Gas Defrost   Hot gas defrost is applicable to all direct expansion types of heat-absorbing surfaces. In this method the heat from the compressor discharge, normally rejected to the condenser or heating surface, is diverted to the outdoor cooling coils.

Perhaps the most convenient way of diverting the refrigerant is by changing from the heating to the cooling cycle, as described in connection with the flow diagram, Figure 3-1 of Chapter 3. The outdoor coil, in this case, becomes the condenser and the conditioner coil the evaporator. This reversal makes available for defrosting the heat removed by the conditioner coil from the air or other medium going to the conditioned space, plus that portion of the heat equivalent of the work of compression which is added to the refrigerant.

The removal of heat from the conditioned space by the conditioner coil in this manner may be objectionable during occupied periods. For this reason, supplemental resistance heat is generally employed to counteract any adverse effect of this cycle. The energy consumption of the supplemental heaters must be included in any cost evaluation.

With this method of defrost the refrigerant gas is delivered to the starved, frosted outdoor coil to give a high condensing rate. Consequently, the expansion valve on the conditioner coil must be selected for proper operation at the resulting low compressor head pressure. In instances where the low head pressure is insufficient to open the expansion valves properly, a bypass, containing an orifice (sized for the correct refrigerant flow) and a shutoff valve ahead of the orifice, is opened for a short period during the defrost cycle.

Circuiting is important in hot gas defrosting. The coils should be self-draining, as mentioned in Chapter 3. Also, an accumulator or suction trap of sufficient size to accommodate the liquid must be provided to prevent slugging due to excessive liquid carry-over to the compressor.

Water Defrost   Water sprays offer a simple and easy method of defrosting an outdoor coil in locations where an ample supply of chemically suitable water at a temperature in excess of 50 F is available. During the defrosting cycle the water is sprayed on the outdoor coil at a rate of approximately 3 gpm per sq ft of coil face area.

The main advantage of the water spray method is the quick response and low first cost. The disadvantage is the probable high operating cost, if city water is employed and if a sewer tax is in effect. Also sand, scale, and other such impurities may cause operating difficulties. It has been observed, in such installations, that a considerable amount of water clings to the coil surface after all the frost is melted and washed down the drain. This wetted surface immediately freezes when the heat pump reverts to the heating cycle and in all probability increases the rate of frost buildup and the number of defrosts required.

Electric Defrost   There are several ways of electrically defrosting the outdoor coil. One method is to locate a bank of infrared elements immediately adjacent to the coil surface. In this method the outdoor coils would be defrosted primarily by radiation from this bank of electric heaters. With sufficient wattage per square foot of coil area, the defrost time can be made equal to or less than that required by the hot gas defrost method. According to limited field tests, the kilowatthours per defrost need not be any greater than for the hot gas method, when energy needed to overcome the cooling effect of the conditioner coil is included.

A second method of defrosting, which has considerable promise, consists of inserting specially designed, sealed tubular electric heaters in the fins to become an integral part of the coil surface. These heaters are spaced throughout the coil to provide an even distribution of radiation, conduction, and convection heat and assure a rapid and positive defrost in a minimum time.

A third possibility is to install several immersion heaters within the tubes of the outdoor coil, or some other part of the refrigerant circuit. The electric heaters could be arranged to heat the refrigerant sufficiently to cause it to boil up through the surface and melt the ice.

Special provisions must be made in the design of the fins and arrangement of the tubes in all these electrical methods in order to provide rapid and unobstructed runoff of the water after defrosting and at the same time to use the heat effectively, without excessive waste to the ambient air.

Solid Adsorbents and Liquid Absorbents   One obvious way to retard frosting is to use adsorbents to remove the moisture from the air before it passes over the outdoor coil. Another method is to use liquid absorbents to flood the surface with a low freezing temperature substance.

In a solid adsorbent system, silica gel, activated alumina or similar material is employed to dehumidify the air before it passes over the outdoor coil and thus avoid frost accumulation. Liquid absorbent is usually a water solution of lithium chloride, calcium chloride, or lithium bromide. The vapor pressure of such a solution is reduced to a suitable level by control of its concentration and temperature.

The water defrost, as well as the adsorbent and absorbent types of systems, is sometimes employed for defrosting low-temperature refrigeration systems. These systems also may be applicable to certain industrial types of heat pump installations. Such applications, however, are not generally practical for residential and commercial comfort heating systems, because of the operating and equipment costs, the complicated automatic controls, and the external source of heat necessary to reactivate the material. Any source of clean heated air at 300 to 350 F can be used for this reactivation.

DEFROSTING CONTROLS

Three control schemes can be used to sense the need for defrosting air source heat pumps and to initiate and terminate the defrost cycle. The length of the defrost cycle is usually 3 to 6 minutes, depending on the method of defrost.

Air Pressure Differential across Coil. Frost accumulation will increase the resistance to air flow across the heat-absorbing coil. A pressure differential switch, therefore, which reacts to the air pressure drop across the coil, can be used to initiate the defrost cycle.

Time Clock. Timers can be used to initiate the defrost cycle at predetermined time intervals, usually 30 to 60 minutes, when outdoor temperatures are below approximately 50 F. This method is positive, but erroneously assumes that the frost accumulation on the surface will generally be at a uniform rate and, consequently, can be satisfactorily defrosted at definite time intervals, regardless of the outdoor temperature. During the cycle the outdoor fans and compressor are stopped, the liquid solenoid valve is closed, and the supplemental heaters can be energized.

Refrigerant-Air Temperature Differential. The suction pressure and corresponding saturated refrigerant temperature decreases with frost accumulation. Therefore, the increase in the differential between the entering outdoor air and the suction pressure (temperature) is an indication of the frost buildup and can be used to initiate the defrost cycle.

The defrosting cycle in all three of the methods is generally terminated by a similar device. This termination can be either by a control sensing the pressure or by a thermostat located to measure the temperature of the liquid refrigerant in the outdoor coil. The defrost of the coil is completed when the temperature (or corresponding pressure) of the liquid leaving the outdoor coil rises to about 50 to 60 F or above.

CONTROL FOR HEATING AND COOLING

The control system to be employed will depend on the operation desired, the performance required, and the type, size, and design of heat pump. The operation can range from manual to completely automatic. A control system can materially effect satisfaction and performance of the installation. It is important, therefore, to use the proper control equipment in order to obtain a flexible and effective heat pump operation. It is very desirable to provide a ready means of switching from heating to cooling, automatic defrosting when air is used as the heat source, and capacity modulation, particularly in the larger sizes of 20 tons and above.

Generally, an all-electric control system is used for the unitary, self-contained equipment. On the larger, central plant type installation, however, either an all-electric or an electric-pneumatic system can be employed.

Normally, provisions should be made in the control system to prevent energizing the supplemental electric heating until the heat pump is unable to satisfy the heating requirements when operating at full capacity, and until the outdoor air is below a predetermined temperature. In this way the coincident electric kilowatt demand and corresponding kilowatthours will be kept to a minimum to obtain the lowest possible operating cost. In some types of installations it may be necessary to energize the supplemental heat during the defrost cycle in order to minimize any cooling effect within the structure; using the supplemental heat in this manner will normally not exceed the maximum demand created during the heating cycle.

An All-Electric Control System. A schematic diagram for an all-electric, air-to-air, unitary heat pump control system is shown in Figure 4-12. It is assumed that the heat pump has a fixed air circuit and the refrigerant flow is reversed to obtain the heating and cooling effect described in connection with Figure 3-1. This control system gives complete automatic operation the year round, after manual switch MS-1 is closed.

Cooling Cycle When the room temperature drops below the setting of thermostat T-1, the indoor fan motor is started through relay E and its contact E-1, and the control equipment is positioned to the cooling cycle by energizing relay A to close contacts A-1 and A-3 and open contact A-2. Closing contact A-3 energizes the outdoor fan motor, and opening contact A-2 breaks the crankcase heater circuit. Closing contact A-1 energizes the compressor starter by means of a

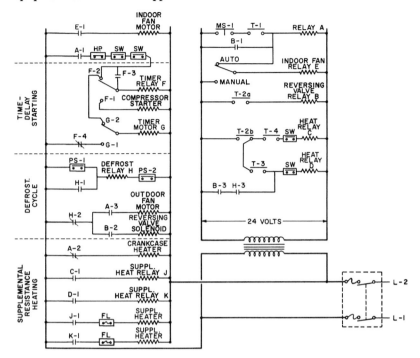

Figure 4-12 Typical schematic diagram for A × 1 all-electric, air-to-air, unitary, heat pump control system.

Relays A: Heating-cooling changeover relay. Relays B: Reversing valve relay. Relays C: Low-voltage supplemental heater relay, 1st stage. Relay D: Low-voltage supplemental heater relay, 2nd stage. Relay E: Indoor fan relay. Relay F: Timer relay for sequence controller. Relay G: Timer motor for sequence controller. Relay H: Defrost relay. Relay J: Line voltage supplemental heater relay, 1st stage. Relay K: Line voltage supplemental heater relay, 2nd stage. Thermostat T-1: Cooling Thermostat. Thermostat T-2a: Heating thermostat, 1st stage. Thermostat T-2b: Heating thermostat, 2nd stage. Thermostat T-3: Outdoor thermostat, closes at about 30°F. Thermostat T-4: Outdoor thermostat, closes at about 20F. Safety Switches: HP—Compressor head pressure switch. Safety Switches: FL—Fusible links, integral part of supplemental heaters. Safety Switches: SW—Safety switch, such as those used to limit motor winding temperatures of compressor discharge temperatures.

two-step sequence controller. The first step energizes timer motor G and timer relay F to open normally closed contact F-4 and to close normally open contact F-3. For step 2, after a predetermined period of time, usually 15 to 30 seconds, the timer switch changes to positions F-1 and G-1 to energize the compressor starter and stop timer motor G. Timer relay F remains energized since contact F-3 remain closed.

This sequence controller is incorporated to prevent short-cycling of the compressor. The timer relay F is de-energized, in case the safety protection switches SW break the circuit for any reason, to open contact F-3 and close contact F-4, which stops the compressor and starts timer motor G. The timer motor G, after about 5 minutes, will reposition the switch to F-2 and G-2, to resume the normal operating sequence, provided all of the safety protection switches SW are closed.

Heating Cycle   When the room temperature drops below the setting of thermostat T-2a, the control equipment is positioned to the heating cycle by energizing reversing valve relay B to close contacts B-1, B-2, and B-3. Closing contacts B-1 and B-2 energize relay A and the reversing valve solenoid to position the four-way refrigerant valve to paths 1-3 and 2-4 as shown in Figure 3-1 of Chapter 3. Closing contact B-3 puts the supplemental heaters under control of the defrost relay H. Energizing the relay A starts the same sequence of operation as described for the cooling cycle.

If the room temperature continues to drop below the setting of T-2b, and the outdoor thermostats T-3 and T-4 are closed, the respective supplemental heaters are energized through heat relays J and K. Fusible links provide overheating protection to the heaters.

Defrost Cycle   The defrost cycle is actuated by the differential air pressure across the outdoor coil. At a predetermined air pressure differential the switch PS-1 actuates the defrost cycle by energizing relay H to open normally closed contact H-2 and to close contacts H-1 and H-3. Opening contact H-2 stops the outdoor fan and positions the reversing valve to the normal cooling position by de-energizing the reversing valve solenoid.

Closing the low-voltage H-3 contacts puts the first step of supplemental heat under control of heating thermostat T-2a.

Supplemental Heating   The supplemental heaters are under control of the second-stage thermostat T-2b. In some instances, outdoor thermostats such as T-3 and T-4 are added to the circuit to prevent operation of the heaters until they are needed as boosters to maintain the desired indoor temperatures. These thermostats are optional, however, and may be omitted to simplify the operation if one single step, representing 15 to 20 kw in most cases, is not objectionable to the electric utility.

It is good practice to add a manual or automatic switch to bypass all interconnecting controls and allow the supplemental heaters to be directly under control of room thermostat T–2a. In case of compressor failure during the emergency cycle, a pilot light should also be energized to show that the heat pump equipment is inoperative and needs attention.

Safety Controls   The safety controls, such as the head pressure controller, the motor winding thermostat, and the discharge temperature thermostat, protect the compressor against abnormal operation. The crankcase heater is always energized during the off cycle to prevent accumulation of the liquid refrigerant in the crankcase. Special features could include solenoid S–2 which permits bypassing the refrigerant throttling valve to the outdoor coil during the defrost cycle in order to provide adequate refrigerant flow under low head pressure conditions. Another special feature is the time delay relay F, which limits compressor short cycling to intervals of 5 minutes or more.

Fusible links are recommended for the supplemental heaters to limit the surface temperature in case the air flow is reduced or interrupted for any reason.

DISTRIBUTION SYSTEMS FOR HEATING AND COOLING

All of the various types of distribution systems used for year-round air conditioning systems are equally applicable to heat pumps, as described in Chapter 7. An indirect water system and/or a forced air system can be used to deliver the heating and cooling effect from the heat pump to the conditioned space. The quantities circulated, the pipe or duct sizes, transfer surfaces, and other such design requirements will closely follow standard practices for cooling systems. Generally, any system which has been designed for conventional comfort cooling will be satisfactory with a heat pump for both heating and cooling.

On the other hand, any heat distribution system designed for a heat pump will be satisfactory for comfort cooling, except perhaps a panel system which normally would require an auxiliary air circulation system to dehumidify the air. Heat pumps can be used with hot and/or cold water indirect systems, high-velocity duct systems, low-velocity duct systems, individual fan-coil conditioners mounted along exterior walls, primary air with induction units, or a combination of any or all of these systems. A number of unitary, self-contained packages, instead of one large central plant, are frequently employed to take full advantage of the flexibility of the heat pump and thereby keep the ductwork, piping, electric power, and control wiring to an absolute minimum.

In order to obtain the most practical overall performance, the maximum supply temperature during the heating cycle is generally limited to 105 to 110 F. This may preclude the use of radiation, such as convectors and finned pipe radiation, but it is ideal for forced air and water systems. Frequently, temperatures of 95 to 105 F are found to be quite satisfactory for most types of heating systems.

A heat pump generally contains little or no reserve heating capacity; consequently, a night setback type of operation is not recommended, particularly during cold weather, unless a storage tank or sufficient supplemental heat is available. Even in these types of applications, care must be exercised because of the possible increase in operating cost due to electric demand charges and other such factors. Some of the more influential factors in connection with storage systems are more fully discussed in Chapters 2 and 8.

REFERENCES

ASHRAE Guide and Data Book (1963), Fundamentals and Equipment, Chap. 58, p. 825.

ASHRAE Guide and Data Book (1964), Applications, Chap. 6, p. 61 and Chap. 75, p. 841.

Brown, George R., Fundamentals of Compound Refrigeration Systems, *Air Conditioning, Heating, and Refrigeration News,* May 11, 1964.

Brown, Leonard N. When And Where to Use Liquid-Suction Heat Interchangers, *Air Conditioning, Heating, and Ventilating,* June 1960.

Goldenberg, David, Conditions that Promote Heat Pump Evaporator Frosting, *Heating and Ventilating,* **61** (January 1952).

Harnish, J. R., Achieving Economy in the Design and Use of Heat Pumps, *Air Conditioning, Heating, and Ventilating,* August 1959.

Healy, James H., Full Season Heat Pump Tests Show Satisfactory Cold-Climate Performance, *American Artisan,* January 1963.

Kramer, D. E., Refrigerant Control in Air-Cooled Condensers, *Refrigerating Engineering,* **41** (July 1958).

Nussbaum, O. J., Adaptability of Air-Cooled Condensers for Large Tonnage Systems, *Refrigerating Engineering,* March 1954.

Ramsey, M. A., Sizing Coil for Near Freezing Air, *Air Conditioning, Heating, and Ventilating,* August 1957.

Sporn, Philip, Ambrose, E. R., and Theodore Baumeister, *Heat Pumps,* John Wiley & Sons, Chap. 6, p. 108, 1949.

Sporn, Philip, and E. R. Ambrose, Two-Year Performance of a Heat Pump System Furnishing Year-Round Air Conditioning in Modern Office Building; *ASHVE Transactions,* 1951.

Stoecker, W. F., How Frost Formation on Coils Affect Refrigeration Systems; *Refrigerating Engineering,* **42** (February 1957).

Chapter 5

Air Conditioning and
Lighting Systems

The trend in modern office and industrial buildings is to minimize the heat loss by using double-glazed windows and additional thermal insulation. Also more and more internal area with the accompanying higher internal heat gain from lights, people, tabulating machines, and similar heat dissipating equipment is being used as office space.

These modern structures must be properly lighted and air conditioned. Correct air conditioning provides the proper thermal environment, and adequate lighting provides the proper luminous environment for greater productivity, accuracy, and comfort. The proper convergence of these two basic components into a comfortable, pleasant, and practical indoor atmosphere can be obtained only by full cooperation between the air conditioning engineer and the illuminating engineer. This cooperation must be based upon a mutual understanding of the common aim, to obtain the most acceptable indoor environment at the lowest possible cost.

Lighting intensities of 50 foot-candles represent about 30 percent of the total summer air conditioning load. This is based on the assumption that all of the heat generated by the lighting and ballast becomes a load on the cooling system. The actual percentage will depend somewhat on the orientation, ratio of the glass to wall areas, shape of the building, the thermal insulation employed in walls and roofs, and the ratio of interior to exterior areas. Twenty-five percent of the remaining portion of the air conditioning load is attributable to the ventilation air, 30 percent to solar and 15 percent to other miscellaneous internal heat gains. As the lighting intensities are raised to 100, 200, 300 and 400 foot-candles, in order to follow the generally accepted trend in commerce and industry, the heat from the lamps and ballast will proportionately increase to about 75 percent of the total summer air conditioning load.

A good portion of the heat can be removed directly from the lighting troffers, as indicated in Figure 5-1, to reduce the initial cost and improve the operating economies. Curve *A* of Figure 5-1 shows the percent increase in the air conditioning load for a particular area, which increases with illuminating levels when all of the lighting heat enters the conditioned space. In contrast, curve *B* shows the comparative increase in the air conditioning load when the lighting heat initially absorbed by the troffers is removed before it enters the conditioned space. For example, trapping the heat at the troffers (curve *B*) with an illumination level of 200 foot-candles (approximately 10 watts per sq ft) will reduce the air conditioned load by 90 percent over

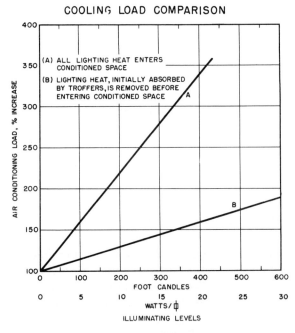

Figure 5-1 Cooling load comparison. (Fisher, Flynn, *General Electric Co. Light Magazine,* **29,** No. 1.)

that required by allowing all the lighting heat to enter the conditioned space (curve A).

It is apparent that these higher lighting levels can be achieved only by developing a practical means of removing or neutralizing a large percentage of the heat from the light. Removing the heat directly from the troffers before it enters the conditioned space can have many beneficial effects including:

1. A substantial heat gain reduction in the room before it becomes a factor in occupant's comfort.

2. Prevention of uncontrolled heat buildup in the lighting system to give more favorable ambient conditions for high efficient operation of lamp and ballast. Flourescent lamps, rated in still air with 77 F ambient, are extremely sensitive to temperature. It is not uncommon for lamps to experience 120 to 130 F temperatures with a corresponding loss in potential light output of 15 to 20 percent. Removing the heat at the source improves the efficiency.

3. The potential application of lighting as a heating system. Higher lighting can furnish much of the structure's heating requirements during cold weather.

4. A reduction in size and operation cost of the installed refrigeration and air handling equipment.

5. Reductions in the size of the building. A material reduction in the overall size of the building can be realized from the smaller air ducts, air shafts and air conditioning equipment.

The theoretical dissipation of heat from a 40-watt fluorescent lamp and ballast (assuming a 50 percent luminaire efficiency) is given in Figure 5-2. Eleven percent of the total energy is due to the ballast, 41 percent to convection and conduction, 15 percent to light and 33 percent to invisible radiation. Of this total, 76 percent or 117 Btuh is initially confined to the luminaire, and 24 percent or 37 Btuh transmitted directly to the conditioned space. Each watt of lamp generates 3.413 Btuh. A ton of cooling is required to remove 3500 watts of lighting regardless of the type of lamp. Fluorescent lamps are more generally used for lighting installations because they have about three times the luminous efficiency of an incandescent lamp. Consequently, this discussion is limited to fluorescent lighting, but many of the comments will also generally apply to other light sources.

Because approximately 76 percent of the conduction, convection, and invisible radiation from the lamps and ballast is initially trapped in the luminaire, the most obvious method of reducing the

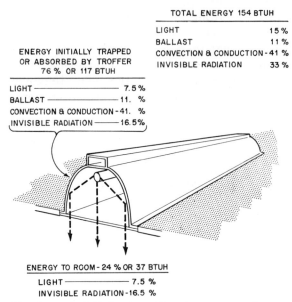

TOTAL ENERGY 154 BTUH

LIGHT	15 %
BALLAST	11 %
CONVECTION & CONDUCTION	- 41 %
INVISIBLE RADIATION	33 %

ENERGY INITIALLY TRAPPED
OR ABSORBED BY TROFFER
76 % OR 117 BTUH

LIGHT	7.5 %
BALLAST	11. %
CONVECTION & CONDUCTION	- 41. %
INVISIBLE RADIATION	16.5 %

ENERGY TO ROOM - 24 % OR 37 BTUH

| LIGHT | 7.5 % |
| INVISIBLE RADIATION | -16.5 % |

Figure 5-2 The theoretical dissipation of heat in a 40-watt fluorescent lamp and ballast (assumed luminaire efficiency—50%). (Fisher, Flynn, *General Electric Co. Light Magazine,* **29,** No. 1.)

adverse effect on the air conditioning system is through removal of the heat energy at the source. Air or water can be used for this purpose.

AIR AS HEAT TRANSFER MEDIUM

The present day conventional comfort cooling installations are generally based on air circulation rates within the conditioned space of 12 to 15 air changes per hour, and on a supply air temperature of about 20 F below the room temperature. Such a design is generally satisfactory for removing the sensible load associated with lighting levels up to 75 foot-candles. Theoretically, the heat from the higher lighting intensities could be handled by raising the air temperature difference up to 30 F or more and/or by increasing the number of air changes. A condition is soon reached, however, as indicated in Figure 5-3, where the first cost and operating cost of the conventional refrigeration and air handling system make the higher lighting intensities almost prohibitive. It can be seen from Figure 5-3 that in going from 50 to 200 foot-candles of lighting the cost of the refrigeration plant is doubled, and the air handling system is increased 2½ times with corresponding higher operating costs.

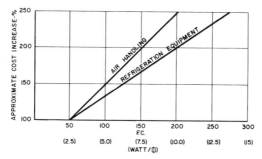

Figure 5-3 The refrigeration and air handling system increases in cost proportionally to increases in foot-candles of lighting. Based on conventional means, the air handling cost increases faster than refrigeration. After Syska and Hennessy, Inc., *Technical Letter,* **10**, No. 1.

One air troffer design which has been found to be effective in removing heat from the lights before it reaches the conditioned space is illustrated in Figure 5-4. The return air from the room, in passing through the luminaires, carries away substantial portions of the heat before it affects room comfort. Glass panels, fused with optical interference coatings, can be further employed to prevent the radiant heat from entering into the room. The heated air from the fixture may be discharged directly to the outside and replaced by outdoor cooler air, or may be circulated through the cooling system when the exhaust temperature is lower than the outdoor air.

The percentage of the trapped heat removed by the return air will depend upon the effectiveness of the fixture to transfer the heat and upon the quantity of air passed through the troffer. Figure 5-5 indicates the approximate amount of heat which can be removed at various air flow rates. It can be noted that exhausting 15 cfm of room

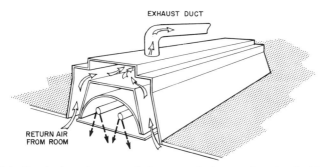

Figure 5-4 Luminaire using room air for removal of trapped or absorbed heat before it enters the occupied space.

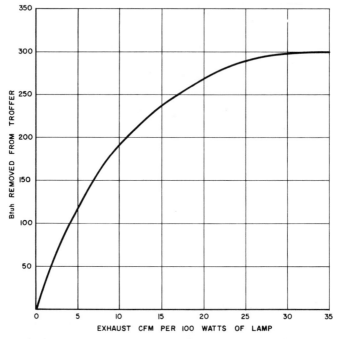

Figure 5-5   Approximate amount of heat which can be removed from troffer at various air flow rates. (Fisher, Flynn, *General Electric Co. Light Magazine,* **29,** No. 1.)

air through the luminaire, for each 100 watts of lamp, will remove approximately 240 Btuh or 62 percent of the total energy of the lamp and ballast. If this air flow rate is increased to 35 cfm per 100 watts of lamp, then about 300 Btuh or 78 percent of the available energy from the lamp and ballast is removed. The air flow is limited by the permissible pressure drop through the troffer and by the possibility of cooling the lamp below the optimum operating temperature.

WATER AS THE HEAT TRANSFER MEDIUM

An alternative (or supplement) to the use of air as the heat transfer medium in light troffers is the use of a water-cooled panel system as illustrated in Figure 5-6. This arrangement can be very effective in the removal of trapped and absorbed heat. The heat from the ceiling panels immediately adjacent to the luminaire can also be cooled by the circulating water. The heat is conducted directly from the troffer and ceiling panels to the water piping system. The water system may consist of integral tubing, (as shown in Figure 5-6) or mechanically attached tubing. Either nonrefrigerated water coolant

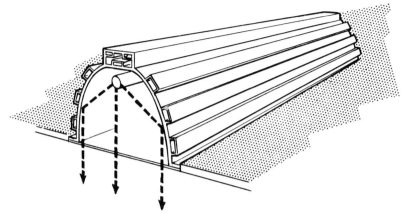

Figure 5-6 Luminaire using circulating water for removal of trapped or absorbed heat before it enters occupied space may have integral tubing, as shown, or mechanically attached tubing

(75 to 85 F) or high-temperature chilled water coolant (60 to 65 F) can be used for this type of application. Because of the water's higher transfer ability, when compared with air, a substantially larger amount of heat can be removed by a relatively small amount of water circulating through the troffer and ceiling panels.

HEAT RECLAIMING CYCLES (*Balancing the Heating and Cooling Load*)

To maintain satisfactory indoor conditions, the structure must be divided into zones with regard to the space requirements. The exterior zones are those areas around the perimeter of the building which are subjected to variations of outdoor temperature and sun effect in addition to the heat gain from the lighting, occupants, business machines, etc. The interior areas include all space enclosed by the exterior zones, usually beginning at the first interior partition which is about 12 to 15 ft from the perimeter wall. The interior areas, except those immediately under the roof, are subjected to the heat gain from the lighting and occupants, and to other internal heat gain, which for all practical purposes is constant the year-round during occupied periods.

If a proper system is not employed for maximum utilization of the heat from the lights and from the other internal heat gains, it may be necessary to follow the wasteful practice of supplying energy to cool interior sections of the building while simultaneously furnishing heat energy to maintain comfortable temperatures in the perimeter portions of the building. There are several heat pump cycles which can be effectively used to transfer heat from the interior of a structure, where cooling is required, to the exterior where heat is needed. Additional heat can also be extracted from discarded ventilation air to precondition incoming ventilation air or to supply other ventilation requirements. Such a pump cycle consists of a vapor compression refrigerating machine, either reciprocating or centrifugal, together with air handlers, fan coil units, circulating pumps, and other such equipment generally used in an indirect cooling system, as shown in Figures 3-8, 3-9, and 3-13 in Chapter 3. One of the most significant benefits of the reclaiming cycle is to limit use of outside supplemental heat by enabling the structure to sustain itself on the heat that is inherent within the structure.

On a clear, cold day the solar radiation, lights, people, and heat generating equipment within the space may offset the negative heat loss of the structure, as illustrated in Figure 5-7. In this example

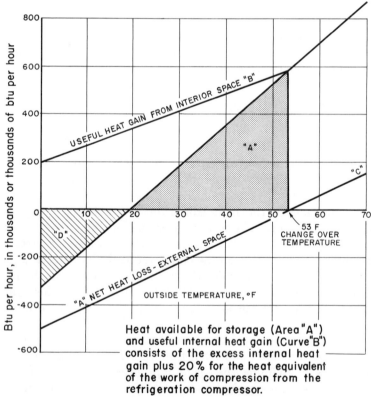

Figure 5-7   Heating and cooling requirements of a structure during occupied periods.

everything below the zero abscissa line represents the additional heat required by the structure, and all above the zero line is usable heat gain from the interior space plus the heat equivalent of the work of compression from the refrigeration compressor. The net heat loss of the perimeter space, curve C, consists of the heat loss, including ventilating air, minus the useful internal heat in the area.

During the occupied winter heating periods, the useful heat gain from the interior space, curve B, balances the net heat loss of the exterior space, curve C, at 19½ F outdoor temperature. From 19½ F to 53 F outdoor temperature, the interior useful heat gain exceeds the exterior heat loss by the amount shown by area A. Above 53 F outdoor temperature (called the changeover temperature) all areas require cooling, and the system changes to the cooling cycle. Below the 19½ F outdoor temperature balance point the exterior heat loss exceeds the interior useful heat gain by the amount shown by area D. During this period heat can be taken from storage, and/or supplemental resistance heat can be used.

During the unoccupied winter periods a large portion of the heat from the lighting and other heat generating equipment will not be available. In these instances, heat can be supplied from the storage tank, by supplemental resistance heat, and/or by an auxiliary heat source.

During the occupied cooling periods, above 53 F outdoor temperature, the refrigeration load varies with the outdoor temperature somewhat as indicated in Figure 4-3 of Chapter 4. It is to be noted that capacity modulation of the refrigeration equipment is very desirable to match the heat gain at various outdoor temperatures.

HEAT RECLAIMING CYCLE DISTRIBUTION SYSTEMS

A number of ways in which the lighting troffers can be incorporated in the air conditioning system to utilize internal heat gain effectively are illustrated in Figures 5-8 through 5-14.

Figure 5-8 shows the conventional method for removing the internal heat gain from a space. Return air from the ceiling plenum mixes with the ventilation air through damper 1, is cooled by conditioner A, and supplied to the conditioned space. The return air removes all possible trapped or absorbed heat in passing through the luminaire. The heat removed by the conditioner's cooling coil is rejected to the outdoor heat sink by means of a direct or indirect refrigeration system. In this cycle all of the internal heat gain is absorbed by the conditioner and cannot be reused for the exterior areas. The total design cooling load which must be handled by the

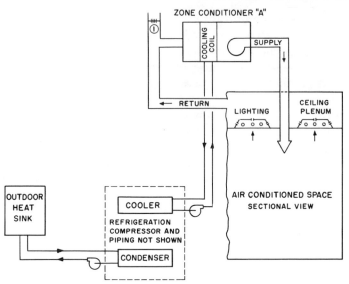

Operation. (1) Air volume damper 1 partially open to permit necessary ventilation air. (2) Return air from ceiling plenum, mixes with ventilation air, is cooled by conditioner "A" and supplied to conditioned space.

General. (1) Mechanical refrigeration equipment must be sized for total cooling load including all heat from the lights. (2) The air quantities can be selected on the basis of the heat gain within the conditioned space (excluding the heat gain in ceiling plenum). (3) Indirect system shown—water or an antifreeze is the transfer medium between refrigerant and the air. (4) Direct expansion may be employed on smaller capacity systems (50 tons and under). In this case refrigerant coils replace the outdoor heat sink unit and the water coils in conditioner "A." The water cooler and condenser are thus eliminated. (5) The surplus heat from interior zones is not reclaimed for the perimeter system—instead it is rejected directly to the outdoor heat sink.

Figure 5-8   Air cooling system—where the total internal gain, including all of the heat from the lights, is absorbed by zone conditioner "A."

mechanical refrigeration equipment must therefore include all of the heat gain from the lights.

The system in Figure 5-9 reclaims the internal heat gain for use by the conditioner *B*. The cooling load from conditioner *A*, plus the heat equivalent of the work of compression, is rejected to the condenser by the refrigeration compressor, and in turn is transferred either to conditioner *B* as useful heat by means of diverting valve 1 or to the outdoor heat sink, as required. In this cycle the mechanical refrigeration system (either direct or indirect) must be sized, also, for the total design cooling load.

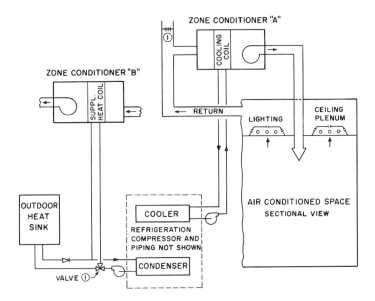

Operation. (1) Air volume damper 1 partially open to permit necessary ventilation air. (2) Return air from ceiling plenum, mixes with ventilation air, is cooled by conditioner "A" and supplied to conditioned space. (3) The cooling load from conditioner "A," plus the heat equivalent of the work of compression, is rejected to condenser, by refrigerating compressor, and in turn transferred to conditioner "B" as useful heat by means of diverting valve 1. (4) When zone conditioner "B" is satisfied, the heat is rejected to a storage tank or to the outdoor heat sink.

General. (1) Mechanical refrigeration must be sized for total cooling load including all heat from lights. (2) The air quantities can be selected on the basis of the heat gain within the conditioned space (excluding the heat gain in ceiling plenum). (3) Indirect system shown—water or an antifreeze is the transfer medium between refrigerant and the air. (4) Direct expansion may be employed on smaller capacity systems (50 tons and under). In this case refrigerant coils replace the outdoor heat sink unit and the water coils in conditioner "A." The water cooler and condenser are thus eliminated. (5) The surplus heat from interior zones can be reclaimed to satisfy other zone conditioners.

Figure 5-9   Air cooling system—incorporating a heat-reclaiming cycle. Total internal gain, including all of the heat from the lights, is absorbed by zone conditioner "A" and transferred to conditioner "B."

Figure 5-10 shows a heat reclaiming cycle which directly utilizes the heat from the lights. Warm return air from the ceiling plenum goes through damper 3 to conditioner B. Air from conditioner B returns through damper 4, mixes with outdoor ventilation air, is cooled by conditioner A, and supplied to the conditioned space. The cooling load from conditioner A is rejected to the condenser by the refrigeration compressor and in turn can be transferred as supplemental heat to conditioner B by means of diverting valve 1 or to the outdoor heat sink, as required. Outdoor air (when about 55 F or below) can be used for comfort cooling with this cycle instead of the mechanical refrigeration system.

In Figure 5-11 the system incorporates a heat reclaiming cycle and directly utilizes the heat from the lights. A large portion of the lighting load is not added to the design mechanical refrigeration load. Instead, during the cooling cycle the outdoor air enters through opening 5, passes through the ceiling plenum, through opening 7, and through the exhaust fan back to the outdoors.

Figure 5-12 also demonstrates a heat reclaiming cycle which directly utilizes the heat from the lights as previously described for the other cycles. In addition, a "run-around" cycle is used to limit the design mechanical refrigeration load to the internal heat gain within the space plus a relatively small portion of the heat from the lights.

In Figure 5-13 there is a heat reclaiming cycle using circulating water in direct contact with the surface of the luminaire or adjacent ceiling panel for removal of trapped or absorbed heat before it enters the conditioned space. The heat taken from the water-cooled luminaire can be transferred to conditioner B or to the outdoor heat sink as required. Similarly, the cooling load from conditioner A is rejected to the condenser by the refrigeration compressor and in turn can be transferred to conditioner B as supplemental heat or to the outdoor heat sink.

Figure 5-14 shows one of the several ways of employing a roof-mounted heat pump to recover heat from the lights before it enters the conditioned space. Instead of the mechanical refrigeration system outdoor air (when 55 F and below) can be used for comfort cooling with this cycle. During the cooling cycle a large part of the lighting load is rejected directly to the outdoors instead of being added to the mechanical refrigeration load.

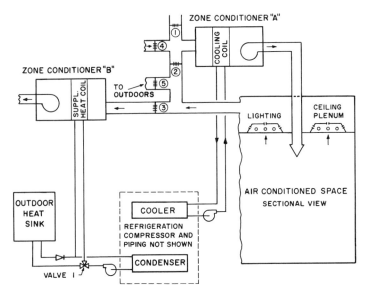

Operation: Heat Reclaiming Cycle. (1) Air volume dampers 3 and 4 open and 1 partially open to permit necessary ventilation. (2) Air volume dampers 2 and 5 closed. (3) Air from zone "B" returns through damper 4, mixes with outdoor ventilation air, is cooled by conditioner "A" and supplied to conditioned space. (4) Warm return air from ceiling plenum goes through damper 3 to conditioner "B."

Operation: Cooling Cycle, For Entire Building. (1) Air volume dampers 3 and 4 closed, exhaust damper 5 open to balance ventilation air intake. (2) Air volume damper 2 open and 1 partially open to permit necessary ventilation. (3) Warm return air from ceiling plenum, mixes with outdoor ventilation air, is cooled by conditioner "A" and supplied to conditioned space.

General. (1) Heat from lights is effectively used for zone "B" during heating cycle. (2) When zone "B" requires cooling the heat from lights becomes a part of the load on the mechanical refrigeration system—except for the small amount exhausted through damper 5 to the outdoors. (3) Indirect system shown—water or an antifreeze is the transfer medium between refrigerant and the air. (4) Direct expansion may be employed on smaller capacity systems (50 tons and under). In this case refrigerant coils replace the outdoor heat sink unit and the water coils in conditioner "A." The water cooler and condenser are thus eliminated. (5) This cycle is very advantageous when the outdoor air is suitable for comfort cooling (about 55F and below). During this cycle the mechanical refrigeration is not required.

Figure 5-10 Air cooling system—incorporating a heat-reclaiming cycle and directly utilizing the heat from the lights.

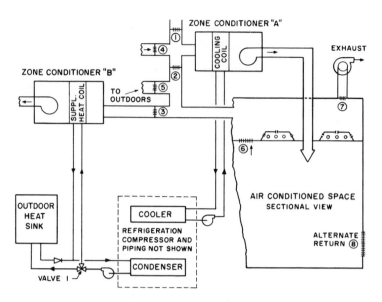

Operation: Heat Reclaiming Cycle. (1) Air volume dampers 3 and 4 open and 1 partially open to permit necessary ventilation. (2) Air volume dampers 2 and 5 closed. (3) Air from zone "B" returns through damper 4, mixes with outdoor ventilation air, is cooled by conditioner "A" and supplied to conditioned space. (4) Warm return air from ceiling plenum goes through damper 3 to conditioner "B."

Operation: Cooling Cycle, For Entire Building (Using Outdoor Air—About 55F and Below). (1) Air volume damper 6 open, dampers 1 and 5 modulate open and 2 modulate close in order to maintain constant air flow to conditioner "A." (2) Air volume dampers 3, 4, 7 and 8 closed. (3) Up to 100 per cent outdoor air enters conditioner "A," through damper 1, and is delivered to conditioned space. (4) Up to 100 per cent warm air from ceiling plenum goes through damper 5 to the outdoors.

Operation—Cooling Cycle (Using Mechanical Refrigeration Cycle). (1) Air volume dampers 4, 5, 7 and 8 open, damper 1 partially open to permit ventilation air. (2) Air volume dampers 2, 3 and 6 closed. (3) Air from conditioned space returns through openings 8 and 4, mixes with outdoor ventilation air, is cooled by conditioner "A" and delivered to conditioned space. (4) Outdoor air enters through opening 5, passes through ceiling plenum, opening 7 and exhaust fan back to the outdoors.

General. (1) Heat from lights is effectively used for zone "B" during the heating cycle. (2) When zone "B" requires mechanical cooling, the heat from the lights, entering the ceiling plenum, is removed by outdoor air. (3) Indirect system shown—water or an antifreeze is the transfer medium between refrigerant and the air. (4) Direct expansion may be employed on smaller capacity systems (50 tons and under). In this case refrigerant coils replace the outdoor heat sink unit and the water coils in conditioner "A." The water cooler and condenser are thus eliminated. (5) The load on mechanical refrigeration is limited to the internal heat gain within the space, including only that portion of the heat from lights that actually enters the conditioned area.

Figure 5-11 Air cooling system—incorporating a heat-reclaiming cycle and directly utilizing the heat from the lights without materially increasing the summer mechanical refrigeration load.

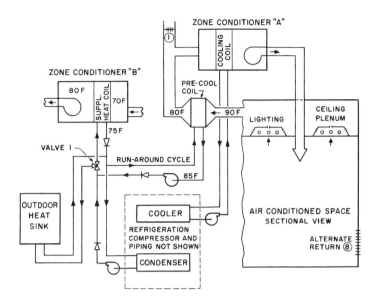

Operation: Heat Reclaiming Cycle. (1) Air volume damper 1 partially open to permit necessary ventilation air. (2) Warm return air from ceiling plenum, passes over precooling coil, mixes with ventilation air, is further cooled by conditioner "A" and then delivered to conditioned space. (3) The heat taken by precooling coils is transferred to conditioner "B" by means of the run-around cycle. (4) The cooling load, from conditioner "A," plus the heat equivalent of the work of compression, is rejected to the condenser, by refrigerating compressor, and in turn transferred to conditioner "B." (5) When zone conditioner "B" is satisfied, the heat is rejected to a storage tank or to the outdoor heat sink.

Operation: Cooling Cycle (Using Mechanical Refrigeration). (1) Air volume damper 1 partially open to permit necessary ventilation air. (2) Warm return air from ceiling plenum passes over precooling coil, mixes with ventilation air, is further cooled by conditioner "A" and then delivered to conditioned space. (3) The heat taken by precooling coil is transferred to outdoor heat sink by means of valve 1. (4) The cooling load, from conditioner "A," plus the heat equivalent of the work of compression, is rejected to the condenser by refrigerating compressor and in turn transferred to outdoor heat sink by means of valve 1.

General. (1) A considerable portion of the heat from lights is effectively used for zone "B" during the heating cycle. (2) Indirect system shown—water or an antifreeze is the transfer medium between refrigerant and the air. (3) Direct expansion may be employed on smaller capacity systems (50 tons and under). In this case refrigerant coils replace the outdoor heat sink unit and the water coils in conditioner "A." The water cooler and condenser are thus eliminated. (4) The load on mechanical refrigeration is limited to the internal heat gain within the space, plus that portion of the heat from the lights not removed by the run-around cycle.

Figure 5-12 Air cooling system—incorporating a heat-reclaiming cycle and directly utilizing the heat from the lights. A "run-around" cycle is used to keep from materially increasing the summer mechanical refrigeration load.

89

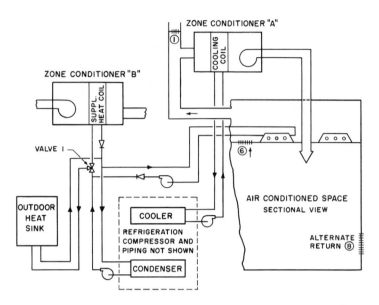

Operation: Heat Reclaiming Cycle. (1) Air volume damper 1 partially open to permit necessary ventilation air. (2) The return air from ceiling plenum, mixes with ventilation air, is cooled by conditioner "A" and delivered to conditioned space. (3) The heat taken from the water-cooled luminaires is transferred to conditioner "B." (4) The cooling load, from conditioner "A," plus the heat equivalent of the work of compression, is rejected to the condenser by refrigerating compressor, and in turn transferred to conditioner "B." (5) When zone conditioner "B" is satisfied, the heat is rejected to a storage tank or to the outdoor heat sink.

Operation: Cooling Cycle (Using Mechanical Refrigeration). (1) Air volume damper 1 partially open to permit necessary ventilation air. (2) The return air from ceiling plenum, mixes with ventilation air, is cooled by conditioner "A" and delivered to conditioned space. (3) The heat taken from the water-cooled luminaires is transferred to outdoor sink by means of valve 1. (4) The cooling load, from conditioner "A," plus the heat equivalent of the work of compression, is rejected to the condenser by refrigerating compressor and in turn transferred to outdoor heat sink by means of valve 1.

General. (1) Heat from lights is effectively used for zone "B" during heating cycle. (2) Indirect system shown—water or an antifreeze is the transfer medium between refrigerant and the air. (3) Direct expansion may be employed on smaller capacity systems (50 tons and under). In this case refrigerant coils replace the outdoor heat sink unit and the water coils in conditioner "A." The water cooler and condenser are thus eliminated. (4) The load on mechanical refrigeration is limited to the internal heat gain within the space, plus that portion of the heat from the lights not removed by the run-around cycle. (5) Water-cooled luminaires provide the most direct method of using the heat gain from the lights. Formation of water-tight circuits through the fixtures, together with a network of water circuits throughout the ceiling, contribute to high fuel cost. In all probability can only be justified for extremely high illumination levels.

Figure 5-13 Air conditioning system in combination with luminaires using circulating water for removal of trapped or absorbed heat before it enters conditioned space.

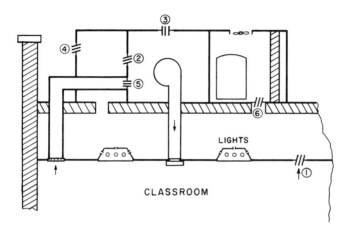

LIGHTS

CLASSROOM

Sectional View

Operation: Heating—Space Occupied. Dampers 4, 5 and 6 tightly closed and 1, 2, 3 open. Return air passes through 1 to pick up heat from lights, then through 2, to mix with outdoor ventilation air coming through 3, then passes over filters, purifier, and heater on way to fan. Supply fan, under control of room thermostat, delivers conditioned air to classroom to complete cycle. Excess air is exhausted to corridor, or as an alternate through damper 6 to outdoors.

Operation: Heating—Space Unoccupied. Dampers 3, 4, 5 and 6 tightly closed and 1 and 2 open. Supply fan circulates air from room, through 1 and 2, over filters, purifier, heater, and back to room in response to room thermostat (night setting).

Operation: Cooling Cycle—with Outdoor Air. Dampers 2 and 6 are closed and 1 and 4 open. Dampers 3 modulates open and 5 close to bring in up to 100% outside air, in response to room cooling thermostat. Supply fan delivers outdoor air through filters and purifier to classroom. Excess air from classroom passes through 1 to pick up heat from lights and is discharged through 4 to the outside.

Operation: Cooling Cycle—with Mechanical Refrigeration. Dampers 1 and 2 closed and 4, 5, 6 open. Damper 3 partially open to admit required ventilation air. Return air passes through 5, mixes with outdoor ventilation air coming through 3, passes over filters, purifier, and cooling coil to supply fan. From fan the conditioned air is supplied to classroom. Outdoor air passes through 4 into ceiling plenum to pick up heat from the lights then through 6 to outdoors.

Figure 5-14   Space conditioners for structures using roof top heat pump units.

REFERENCES

Browder, Joe B., Foot Candles–The Key to Competition, *Edison Electric Institute Bulletin,* May 1963.

Fisher, W. S., and J. E. Flynn, Integrated Lighting–Air Conditioning Systems, *Light Magazine,* **29,** No. 1.

Hill, Neil, Heat Pump Reclaim System Proves New Design Approach, *Heating, Piping and Air Conditioning,* September 1960.

Kridel, N. T., and L. C. Twichell, Remodeling for High Comfort . . . , *Illuminating Engineering,* **LVI,** No. 8 (August 1961).

Meckler, Gershon and J. S. Hickman, Radiant Control of Lighting Heat Loads, *Illuminating Engineering,* **LVI,** No. 8 (August 1961.)

Quin, M. L., and R. D. Bradley, "Convective Transfer of Lighting Heat Load," Paper presented at the National Technical Conference of Illuminating Engineering Society, September 24–29, 1961.

Roberts, G. G. M., The Problems of Heat Gain from High Level Illumination, *Heating and Air Conditioning,* December 1963.

Tamblyn, R. T., Bootstrap Heating for Commercial Office Buildings, *ASHRAE Transactions,* 1963.

Thomas, C. C., How Heat Gains Effect Fuel Bills, *Air Conditioning, Heating and Ventilating,* November 1963.

Weast, John, Control Tips for Radiant Ceiling Panels, *Air Conditioning, Heating and Ventilating,* December 1961.

Chapter 6

Electric Resistance Heating:
Design and Application.
Heat Conservation Practices

In many areas of the world, resistance type of electric space heating has become an acceptable method of heating residences as well as commercial and industrial structures. The resistance heating units are generally selected for those applications where heating only is desired but can be practical and economically combined with electric cooling equipment to furnish year-round air conditioning. The attractiveness of resistance electric heating is further enhanced by the fact that it can be used as a supplement to the heat pump to give a number of desirable advantages over other types of systems.

INDIVIDUAL ROOM UNITS

The great majority of available, individual room types of equipment can be normally classified as heating cable, natural convection, forced convection, baseboard, and radiant. The recommended locations of these general types of electric heaters are shown in Figure 6-1.

1. *Heating Cable.* Heating cable is particularly adaptable to new construction and can be embedded in the ceilings, floors, or sidewalls to supply uniform heat over the entire area. The 120- or 240-volt cable is approximately ⅛ to ¼ in. in diameter and usually is covered with a plastic insulation. It is available in a variety of lengths, from 17 to 2600 ft, with an approximate heating effect of 2.8 watts per linear foot. The heating cable is laid back and forth on the flat surface with a definite space between turns, and the heating output in each area can be under control of an individual thermostat.

2. *Convectors.* Convectors, natural or forced, for wall mounting, consist of a coil of high-resistance wire wound around a porcelain or ceramic tube or of an insulated wire embedded in a finned metal

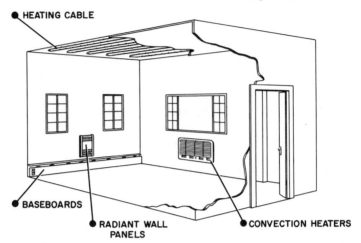

Figure 6-1 Isometric view of a space showing the preferable location of the various direct electric heating units. (Sporn and Ambrose, *Air Conditioning, Heating and Ventilating,* July 1960.)

casing. In some types, a polished sheet of metal is placed behind the heating metal to act as a reflector. These heaters have one or more heating elements that range in total capacity from 1 to 8 kw, although 4 kw is usually the maximum recommended for residential use.

3. *Baseboard.* Baseboard natural convection units can be either recessed or surface-mounted along the exterior wall. The units have a length of about 2 to 12 ft and vary in height from 3½ to 10 in. The heating elements are rated from 100 to 400 watts per linear foot and operate at either 120 or 240 volts. The heaters may be controlled by either a line or low-voltage, wall-type thermostat or by a specially designed thermostat located in the baseboard section.

4. *Radiant.* Radiant wall panels can be either glass, ceramic, or metal alloy for recessed or surface mountings. These panels are of many sizes, shapes, and designs, and the temperature when they are energized is usually in the neighborhood of 325 to 400 F. The heaters are sized from 500 to 3000 watts at 120 or 240 volts and are controlled by either low-voltage or line-voltage thermostats.

CENTRAL ELECTRIC FURNACES

Unquestionably, the full utilization of the many inherent operating advantages of the individual room type of equipment to generate heat when and where needed has contributed greatly to the public acceptance of this type of electric heating. In this respect, the electric furnace is not so efficient or advantageous as the individual room type of heating unit, since it generally must be remotely located and connected to a forced air distribution system. Such systems, on the other hand, can provide air circulation, filtering and humidification as required and, with the addition of a coil-condensing unit combination, also will supply cooling to the occupied space.

The central electric furnace also offers attractive first cost possibilities, and its operating cost need not be appreciably higher than the individual room type of unit, if a well-designed and thoroughly insulated distribution system is employed. The importance of using an approved method of delivering the heating medium to and from the occupied space can not be overemphasized. Proper precautions must be taken to minimize the distribution losses and to prevent the overheating of the space that may be due to the orientation of the structure. If this is not done, the forced warm air type of system will certainly cause considerable dissatisfaction and excessive operating costs. The various design and application practices for forced air type of distribution systems are more fully covered in Chapter 7.

CENTRAL ELECTRIC BOILERS

Numerous types and sizes of steam and hot water boilers are available for both residential and commercial applications. The electric boiler type of system can be quite flexible in design and arrangement. The hot water boilers are particularly adaptable to a hydronic heating and cooling application. In this instance, the same water quantities and the same piping system can be used for delivering the heating and cooling effect to the conditioned space. Perhaps the chief attraction of a hydronic system is the zoning and capacity modulation that can be readily supplied.

An electric steam or hot water boiler can be combined also with a forced air cooling system. Steam or water from the boiler can be delivered to coils which are installed in the branch ducts immediately back of the supply grilles, and/or in the main ducts remotely located from the conditioned space. In this way, the duct system can frequently be simplified and at the same time all of the advantages of a forced air circulation system are obtained. Additional details of the several types of steam and hot water systems are given in Chapter 7.

ELECTRIC DUCT HEATERS

Small, forced air type heaters can be installed in ducts in the same manner as that described for steam and hot water coils. Fully utilizing the many inherent possibilities of this type of heater can give electric heating a decided advantage over other types of systems.

These duct heaters are available in a multiplicity of sizes and designs. They can be located nearly anywhere—in the branch ducts behind the supply grille, in the main ducts, and/or in the air conditioner. For full acceptance, these heaters must have all of the safety features as well as the Underwriters' Laboratory approval.

The electric resistance type of duct heater can be used as a booster to an electric furnace or heat pump unit, as a preheater for ventilation air, or for reheat during the cooling cycle. Nearly every heat pump installation employs one or more booster duct heaters in order to obtain a practical and flexible system. Since no freezing damage is possible, this type of heater is particularily attractive for preheating the ventilation air. Electric duct heaters are also extensively used in constant humidity type of applications for preheating the supply air during the cooling cycle, after it has been lowered in temperature for removal of excess moisture. A more extensive discussion of these and other types of duct heater installations is given in Chapter 7.

APPLICATION CONSIDERATIONS
FOR HEAT CONSERVATION

The recommended and acceptable fundamentals for calculating the heating requirements and for obtaining a correct application of the equipment must be understood to insure a satisfactory and acceptable installation. In many comfort heating systems, particularly with electric heating, the resulting reduction in both the initial cost and the annual energy cost is sufficient economic justification to incorporate and make full use of the many available heat saving devices such as:

1. Full utilization of ceiling, exterior walls, and floor insulation.
2. Effective use of weather-stripped windows and doors and of insulating glass and storm sash.
3. Reducing infiltration or ventilation air requirements to a minimum, by means of air purification equipment.
4. Employment of exhaust-ventilation heat exchangers.

Thermal Insulation. Perhaps the most attractive of these heat saving devices is the use of thermal insulation not only to minimize the winter heat loss but also to reduce materially the summer heat gain, with a corresponding reduction in the size and operating cost of the heating and cooling equipment. In addition, insulation improves the indoor comfort by maintaining the inside surface temperature of the structure, close to the indoor temperature. The temperature of the inside room surface has an adverse effect on human comfort, which is independent of the ambient temperature and air motion. The lower the surface the higher the degree of discomfort experienced, because of radiation effect between the surface and occupant. Also, the warm surface temperature, during cold weather, will minimize the flow of cold air down the outer walls and across the floor with the accompanying discomfort.

The importance of full insulation can be illustrated by comparing the effect of various thicknesses of insulation on the heating requirements of a house. Figure 6-2 is such a comparison for a typical ranch type house with an indoor-outdoor design temperature difference of 75 F. The possible Btuh heat loss reduction from an uninsulated structure because of the insulation, the reduction in the infiltration and the windows and storm doors represented by D is 74,085 or 71 percent. In an area with 5700 degree days and 1.5 cents per kwhr electric energy rate, the estimated resistance heating annual operating cost of this structure would be reduced from $647 for the uninsulated house to $184 for the D insulated structure, a reduction of $463 per year. Another significant saving, realized with full insulation, is the reduction in the cost of the heating equipment, which in the example would represent about $400. For this particular structure, the additional cost of the thermal insulation was estimated

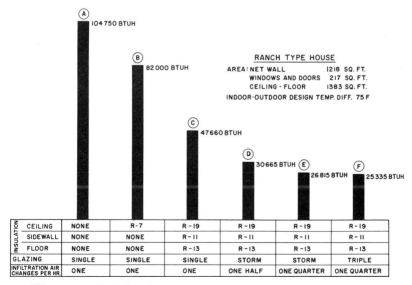

Figure 6-2   Btuh heat loss comparison with various types of insulation.

at \$675 and the storm windows and doors at \$450 for a total of \$1125. The saving in the first cost of the equipment, due to the lower heat loss, is \$400 to give a net additional cost of \$725. Therefore, since the annual operating cost saving is \$463, the first cost of the insulation and storm doors and windows can be amortized in less than two years.

The justification for the maximum thickness of thermal insulation, storm doors, and double or triple glazed windows with the best weather stripping will depend upon the type and kind of structure, the electric energy cost, the severity of the outdoor temperature, and

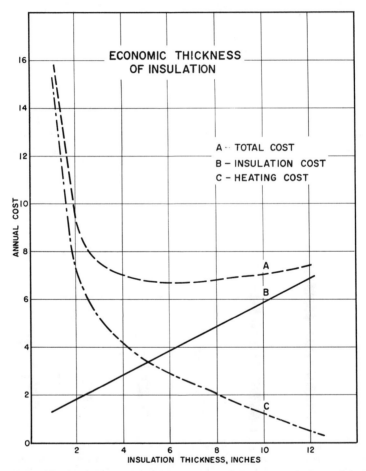

Figure 6-3 Relation between optimum thickness of thermal insulation and the heating cost, insulation cost, and total cost.

on the first cost of the material and equipment. For residences the recommended minimum amount of ceiling insulation will generally result in an overall U value of 0.05 and an R value of 19; for walls a U of 0.08 with and R11 value; and for floors a U of 0.10 with a R13. The R value may be defined as the installed thermal resistance of the insulation.

The optimum thickness of thermal insulation can be related to the annual cost of the investment as illustrated in Figure 6-3. The cost factors for curve C include energy cost, capital investment, cost of money, interest, depreciation, maintenance, and hours of operation. The cost factors for curve B include capital investment, cost of money, interest depreciation, and maintenance. The total cost curve A is the sum of the other two curves. The minimum point in this curve represents the optimum insulation thickness. Plotting such a family of curves for a particular structure can be a laborious task. Such an exploration over a wide range of conditions is unnecessary if only the optimum insulation is required. This can be obtained directly by the use of the following mathematical formulas which have been developed by several investigators.

$$R_0 = \frac{[A][(C)(DD)(P)+(M)(\Delta T)(Q)]}{(R_G)(3413)(M)(Z)} \qquad (6\text{-}1)$$

where $R_0 =$ equivalent economic thermal resistance
$A =$ area under consideration, sq ft
$C =$ NEMA operating cost factor, 16 to 24
$DD =$ winter degree days, 65 F base
$P =$ power rate for electric space heating, dollars/kw
$M =$ payment per year, for first cost: principal and interest (dollars/dollar)
$\Delta T =$ design temperature difference, of
$Q =$ installed cost of incremental unit of heating equipment, dollars/kw
$R_G =$ base thermal resistance of the building section (to which base other levels of thermal performance are compared)
$Z =$ installed cost per incremental unit of thermal resistance of insulation over the area, A-, dollars

Insulation, in addition to the desired thermal values, must have several other inherent characteristics. It must be noncombustible, not subject to rot or decay, moisture resistant, and neither attractive to nor a harbor for vermin. High chemical and physical stability and high dielectric properties are essential.

Some insulation materials are impervious to moisture penetration and need no vapor barrier, but generally a suitable vapor barrier should be applied to the warm side of the structure. The permeance of the vapor barrier should be 1 perm or less, such as can be obtained with polyethylene film, plastic or metal foils. The part of the wall exposed to the outdoors should have a permeance of at least 5 perms, so that moisture vapor getting through the inside barrier can readily escape to the outside.

When insulation is used above the ceiling area, the attic should be vented to the outside, and, plastic film should cover the ground in the crawl space beneath the floor of the structure, to avoid condensation with resulting inefficiency of insulation and deterioration of the framing.

Storm Windows and Doors. Sufficient thermal insulation on the exterior walls of a structure is extremely important, but proper consideration for the reduction in the heat loss and gain through windows and doors is equally important as indicated in Figure 6-2. With proper evaluation, it will usually be concluded that insulating glass or double-glazed windows and doors can easily be justified in most areas, and triple-glazed windows will frequently be found practical in many northern sections of the United States.

In addition to reducing the heating and cooling loads, storm windows are generally the most economical method of minimizing window condensation. Visible condensation occurs when the temperature of any surface is below the dew point of the nearby air. The indoor relative humidity at which visible condensation appears, with a fixed indoor temperature, will vary directly with the outdoor temperature and inversely with the heat transmittance U as illustrated in Figure 6-4. It can be noted from this graph that with a 30 percent indoor relative humidity, condensation will form on single glass when the exterior temperatures are 23 F or lower. In contrast, with double glazing an indoor relative humidity of 30 percent can be maintained with outdoor temperatures down to 30 F below zero. With triple glazing, relative humidities of 50 percent, or even higher, could be maintained without fear of condensation at temperatures far below zero. These results will, of course, be affected by curtains, draperies, venetian blinds, and the ability of the heating equipment, because of its location, to blanket the exposed surfaces.

The chief cause of condensation is not always the glass itself. As shown in Figure 6-4, condensation may form on aluminum or steel sash if the indoor relative humidity is approximately 27 percent and the outdoor temperature is 20 F or lower. Wood sash is more

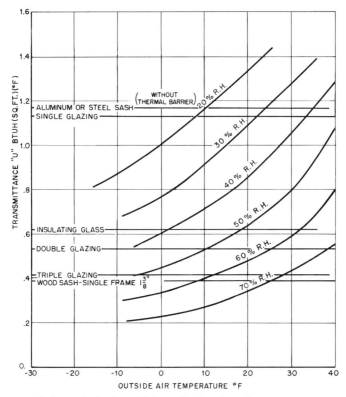

Figure 6-4 Indoor relative humidities and related outdoor temperatures at which visible condensation will appear on inside surfaces with various heat transmittance "U." 70F inside air temperature. After ASHRAE *Guide and Data Book,* 1963, Chap. 6, Fig. 4.

favorable in this connection, since condensation will not form even if the indoor humidities rise above 65 percent. Consequently, to prevent excessive condensation, it is generally recommended that the rate of heat transmission through the prime sash and frame be equal to, or lower than, the glass. This means that metal sash must have an effective thermal barrier with an acceptable heat transmittance value to minimize structural heat loss and to keep the inside surface temperature above the dew point of indoor air.

Infiltration and Moisture Levels in Residences. One of the major factors contributing to a high heating and cooling operating cost is excessive infiltration of air. This undesirable condition can be reduced by weather stripping and by using double-glazed windows and doors. In addition, all exhaust openings from the structure, such as chimneys for open fireplaces, should be equipped with well-fitting dampers which are kept tightly closed except when in use.

Fireplace enclosures offer a very economical means of heat conservation. A wood-burning fireplace can be a very costly and undesirable form of heating if it at the same time creates uncomfortable floor drafts and causes warm air to be drawn up the flu and wasted. One remedy is the use of a tempered glass fireplace enclosure equipped with adjustable draft doors to regulate the amount of combustion air taken from the room. Another possibility is an inner wall firebox which is designed to circulate warm air, by gravity, to and from the room. Either device will tend to offset the cold drafts produced by an open fireplace.

It is apparent that as the infiltration rate decreases in a residence, the indoor humidity level increases because the moisture generated by cooking, bathing, laundering, dishwashing, etc. is not removed so rapidly. This increase in indoor relative humidity is desirable up to a certain point. It is generally accepted that a range of 30 to 50 percent, with a corresponding indoor dry bulb temperature of 70 to 75 F, is the optimum for comfort and health. Under certain conditions, the moisture generated by appliances and the living habits of the household, as indicated in Table 6-1, may create excessive relative humidities.

TABLE 6-1

Cooking, including dish washing	5.66 lb/day
Washing, ironing, indoor drying family of four	30.73 lb/week
Bath	0.5 lb/shower
	1.12 lb/bath
People for 24-hour period.	5.7 lb/person
Floor washing, each washing	8.0 lb/100 sq ft
Flower watering	1.84 lb/plant

One common method of lowering the relative humidity within the occupied space is to vent the moisture producing appliances to the outside. This method is not very economical, since an equal quantity of outdoor air, with the accompanying dirt and other impurities contained in the atmosphere, must be introduced into the residence to increase the filtering, heating, and cooling requirements. A more acceptable and satisfactory solution is to incorporate a dehumidifier-filter-odor removing unit as part of the heating and cooling system. This can generally be a small, self-contained, independent, forced circulation type of unit, located in the vicinity of the moisture-producing appliance.

Such a unit is very practical, since the dehumidifier removes the excess moisture and, at the same time, returns the latent heat of vaporization to the space, in the form of useful heat. The filter and the odor absorber, on the other hand, maintain a clean and odorless environment. In this way, electric heating systems can control, simultaneously, the temperature, humidity, cleanliness, and air circulation and thus overcome one of the criticisms sometimes directed toward the in-the-space type of electric heating.

Cost of Excessive Ventilation Air. A worthwhile reduction in the first cost and operating cost can frequently be realized during both the heating and the cooling cycles by the proper selection of the ventilation air quantities. In many instances, the commonly used ventilation air quantities are governed neither by the oxygen requirements nor by the carbon dioxide liberated, which for normal activity total about 0.89 and 0.74 cu ft per man-hour, respectively, but instead by the odors rising from the occupancy, living habits, smoking, or other such sources. The reduction or control of these odors is generally attempted by introducing air in sufficient quantities to dilute the odor concentration to a nonobjectionable level. Such odor-free air may be outdoor air, but the preferable and positive way is to employ odor absorbing materials.

Unfortunately, there are no generally accepted procedures for predetermining the correct amount of ventilation air for any given application and, consequently, the amount selected in many instances depends upon the individual experience and preference of the design engineers. The ventilation air requirements for human occupancy are a function of the space per person and the activity, as shown by Figure 6-5. Some minimum outdoor requirements (during the heating season), established back in 1936 under laboratory conditions and shown as curve C of the figure, vary from 8 cfm per person for a volume of 400 cu ft to 25 cfm per person with 100 cu ft of space. In contrast, present day practice indicates ventilation air quantities, during the cooling cycle, in general office areas with some smoking, of 15 cfm per person, with a minimum of 10 cfm. For private offices with no smoking the recommended figures increase to 25 cfm per person and, with considerable smoking, to 30 cfm, or 0.25 cfm per sq ft of floor area, whichever is the greater.

This "rule of thumb" method of determining the ventilation requirements disregards the available cubic foot of space per person (which is related to the ventilation requirements as shown in Figure

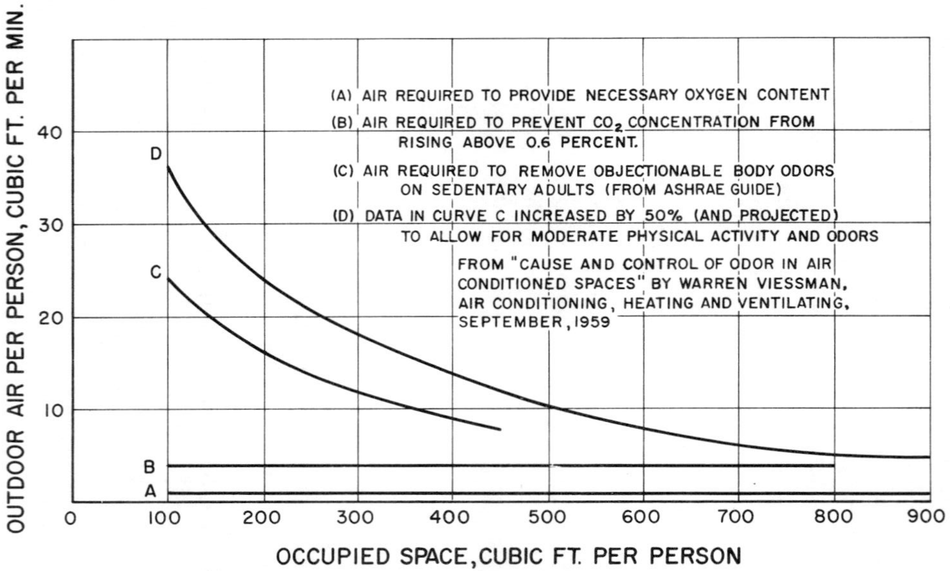
(A) AIR REQUIRED TO PROVIDE NECESSARY OXYGEN CONTENT
(B) AIR REQUIRED TO PREVENT CO_2 CONCENTRATION FROM RISING ABOVE 0.6 PERCENT.
(C) AIR REQUIRED TO REMOVE OBJECTIONABLE BODY ODORS ON SEDENTARY ADULTS (FROM ASHRAE GUIDE)
(D) DATA IN CURVE C INCREASED BY 50% (AND PROJECTED) TO ALLOW FOR MODERATE PHYSICAL ACTIVITY AND ODORS
FROM "CAUSE AND CONTROL OF ODOR IN AIR CONDITIONED SPACES" BY WARREN VIESSMAN, AIR CONDITIONING, HEATING AND VENTILATING, SEPTEMBER, 1959
D
C
B
A
OUTDOOR AIR PER PERSON, CUBIC FT. PER MIN.
10
20
30
40
0
100
200
300
400
500
600
700
800
900
OCCUPIED SPACE, CUBIC FT. PER PERSON

Figure 6-5 Ventilation requirements related to cubic feet of occupied space per person. After Viessman, *Air Conditioning, Heating, and Ventilating,* September 1959.

6-5) and thereby frequently results in excessive ventilation air. Even so, some design engineers work on the theory that if 15 to 30 cfm per person, for instance, is accepted practice, than 40 to 60 cfm will be better. There are no available data, however, which indicate that more healthy and acceptable conditions will result with increased air quantities, and actually there is no factual information to indicate an adverse effect if the quantities are reduced. It does appear axiomatic, therefore, that reasonable ventilation quantities, without the sacrifice of a healthful environment, should be selected to obtain a minimum first cost and operating cost.

Even minimum quantities of outdoor air may be unacceptable, however because of the objectionable, irritable, and toxic odors in the atmosphere, due to a high percentage of hydrogen sulphide, smog, effluence from industrial processes, automobile exhaust, and other such chemical by-products. It is because of this possibility that physical or chemical odor removal units are increasing in popularity.

It has been found that an absorbing material such as activated charcoal together with a conventional air filter or an electric filter is quite effective in removing tobacco smoke and other odor-causing substances. Actual air conditioning designs for different types of applications show savings in both initial and operating cost, by reducing the quantity of ventilation air and passing the equivalent amount of recirculated air through carbon filters as shown in Figure 6-6.

Each 1000 cfm reduction of outdoor air, for example, will represent a saving of about 3 tons in refrigeration equipment and 80 mbtuh in heating equipment, with a corresponding annual operat-

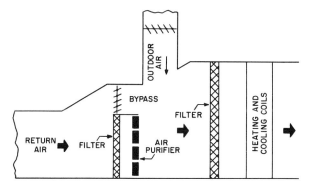

Figure 6-6   Reducing outdoor air quantities to a minimum by means of activated charcoal filters. Air purifier can be installed to decontaminate a percentage of the return air, if the outdoor air is objectionably contaminated.

ing cost saving of about $450 when a heat pump with electric energy costing 1½ cents per kwhr is used. The investment in a charcoal filter installation, including the average annual cost of reactivation and maintenance, is about $300. The initial cost of the air purifier can therefore be amortized in less than a year by the resulting savings in operating cost. In addition, there is considerable saving in the first cost of heating and cooling equipment.

Ventilation for Kitchens and Industrial Processes. Many excellent examples of excessive outdoor air usage can be found in commercial and industrial applications. In many instances, ventilation air quantities for kitchens and industrial applications are enormous, and frequently the heat required to temper the air will exceed all of the other heat losses of the structure. Fortunately, there are several practical and attractive methods for achieving considerable savings, including:

1. Injecting untempered supply air into hot areas or over hot equipment, so as to pick up the heat without causing uncomfortable working conditions.
2. Heating the supply air with waste gases or hot discharged air by means of a heat exchanger.
3. Employing vented hoods over heat-producing equipment.

Perhaps the third suggestion, employing vented hoods to reduce the ventilation requirements, offers the most attractive possibilities for the normal type of commercial or industrial application. Attractive and structurally acceptable hoods are frequently used in hotel and restaurant kitchens, for instance, but relatively little information is available on effective methods for entraining and exhausting the fumes from localized areas, with a minimum consumption of room air. Carelessness and over liberal designs of hoods not only result in fantastic ventilating air requirements with corresponding high initial and operating costs, but create formidable problems of introducing the make-up in the space. Large hoods require less air per unit volume than smaller ones, as illustrated in Figure 6-7. This figure shows the relationship between air velocity at hood opening and distance between hood opening and working surface. It can be noted that the ratio of length to width, as well as the distance above the work surface, affects the required velocity of the hood opening. The curves in Figure 6-7 are based on a 30 fpm velocity above operating periphery. Velocities below 30 fpm, even as low as 10 fpm, have been found to be adequate if the open areas not in use are covered with a suitable metal shield. With these lower periphery velocities,

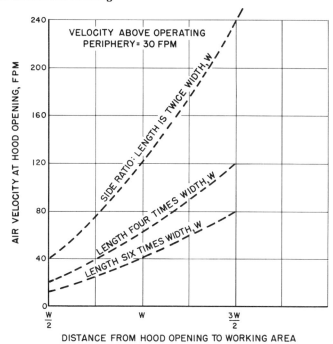

Figure 6-7 Relation between air velocity at hood opening and distance to working surface—expressed in terms of hood width *W* for rectangular hoods with different side ratios. (Sporn and Ambrose, *Air Conditioning, Heating, and Ventilating,* July 1960. From design of kitchen range hood, J. M. Dallavalle, *Heating and Ventilating,* August 1953.)

the required air velocity at the hood opening is proportionally reduced. For example, for a hood with a length six times the width and at a height *W* above working area, changing the periphery velocity from 30 to 10 fpm will cause a corresponding reduction in the velocity at the hood opening from 40 to 13.4 fpm.

In some instances, unheated outdoor air can be introduced, as shown in Figure 6-8, to prevent drafty conditions in the kitchen and, at the same time, to make a material reduction in the heating requirements. In such an arrangement it is often feasible to use 65 percent of the ventilation air directly from the outside and only 35 percent from the surrounding area.

HIGH-TEMPERATURE INFRARED RADIANT SYSTEMS

Another form of electric heating that is finding increasing acceptance in many industrial and commercial comfort heating applications is the high-intensity infrared radiant heating unit. In

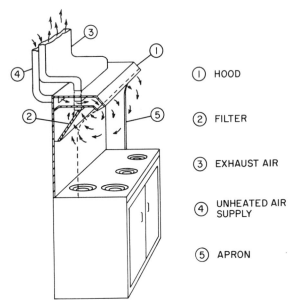

1. HOOD

2. FILTER

3. EXHAUST AIR

4. UNHEATED AIR SUPPLY

5. APRON

Figure 6-8 A suggested method of providing unheated outdoor air for hood ventilation to minimize the make-up air requirements and to effect an appreciable heating and cooling cost saving. (Sporn and Ambrose, *Air Conditioning, Heating, and Ventilating,* July 1960.)

contrast to the low-temperature floor radiant systems covered in Chapter 2, which often required utilization of the full floor or ceiling area to obtain sufficient heating effect, the high-temperature units emit a much greater quantity of thermal radiation per unit area.

These high-temperature units, as shown in Figure 6-9, resemble fluorescent lighting fixtures and are scientifically designed to enable the long-wave infrared rays to pass through cold air and warm objects which fall within its focused beam. This optically engineered reflector thus insures a maximum radiant effect with a minimum transfer of convection and conduction heat to the ambient. The pure, fused quartz tube heating element is a refractory material which can withstand temperatures up to 1800 F. The quartz envelope resists thermic shock and will withstand ice cold water sprays without damage, and thus is suitable for either indoor or outdoor application in the coldest of climates.

High-temperature infrared heating can be used for many comfort heating installations, including spot heating in warehouses, machine shops, stadium grandstands, bus stations, theatre marquees, barns, churches, railroad stations and repair shops, swimming pool perimeters, iron and steel foundries, and all areas which may be difficult to heat because of possible stratification. This type of heating is particularly applicable for warming workers in open and semi-open areas, such as loading docks or buildings where large doors are frequently opened. Since comfort can be achieved with spot heating, without proportionally raising the ambient temperature, the operating cost can be materially lower than that of convection heating. Other advantages, in addition to operating cost, include reduction in cleaning and maintenance cost, ease and economy of the installation, and elimination of obstructions in the working area.

Some experience is essential in designing these installations, and the heater manufacturers should be consulted. Consideration should not only be given to the building heat loss but to the radiant intensity at the working level where the heating is desired. It should be noted that good insulating practices are also beneficial in this type of heating. A loading of 12 to 20 watts per sq ft is normally used in a reasonably well-insulated building in continuous use. This intensity is often increased to 30 to 50 watts per sq ft for heating localized work areas or the areas adjacent to the perimeter of the building.

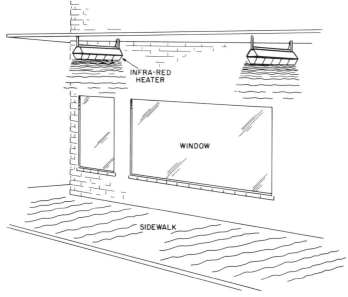

Figure 6-9 Infrared electric heating for snow melting on sidewalks and for warming workers in open areas.

REFERENCES

Ambrose, E. R., Electric Space Heating—The Concept of Total Heat Conservation, *Electric Light and Power,* February 1964.

Analysis of Electric Energy Usage in Air Force Houses Equipped with Air-to-Air Heat Pumps, NBS Monograph 51, U.S. Department of Commerce, National Bureau of Standards, July 13, 1962.

Boyd, R., and A. Johnson, *Insulation Economics of Electric Heat,* American Institute of Electrical Engineers Conference Paper, CP 62 401, 1962.

Cablentz, C. and P. Achenback, Field Measurements of Air Infiltration in Ten Electrically Heated Houses, *ASHRAE Transactions,* **69** (1963).

Goff, James F., Insulate to Afford Electric Heat, *Electric Heat,* July 1955.

Jordan, R. C., G. A. Erickson, and R. R. Leonard, Energy Sources and Requirements for Residential Heating, *ASHRAE Transactions,* **68** (1962).

Jordan, R. C., G. A. Erickson, and R. R. Leonard, Infiltration Measurements in Two Research Houses, *ASHRAE Transactions,* **69** (1963).

Rysselberge, J. R., and S. R. Hribar, Seeing Fuel Competition in the Right Perspective, *Public Utilities Fortnightly,* **70** (November 22, 1962).

Tamura, G. T., and A. G. Wilson, Air Leakage and Pressure Measurements on Two Occupied Houses, *ASHRAE Journal,* December 1963.

Thomas, C. C., How Much Insulation Should Be Used in Electrically Heated Buildings, *Air Conditioning, Heating and Ventilating,* March 1961.

Chapter 7

Heating and Cooling
Distribution Systems

Some precautions must be exercised when the heating and cooling functions are incorporated in the same distribution system. The usual practice is to select equipment of adequate size and design to satisfy either the heating or the cooling requirement, whichever is the larger. Generally, in the case of the heat pump, the system capacity is dictated by the cooling load. Because of the orientation, exposure, and internal heat gain of the different areas, zoning is necessary to maintain uniform indoor conditions. Frequently, owing to economic considerations, zoning is not employed for residential and small commercial installations. In such cases some manual adjustments in air or water flow are often necessary in the change from one cycle to another, to compensate for the unbalanced heating and cooling requirements. Such manual adjustments seldom result in satisfactory indoor conditions. Electric booster heaters in such instances can often be used advantageously within the space, in a branch duct, or in a water pipe to overcome the unbalance between the heating and the cooling loads.

RESIDENTIAL SYSTEMS

The general types of heating and cooling systems available for most residential installations are:

1. Forced air distribution
2. Hydronic
3. Individual self-contained room units

Forced Air Distribution. The heat pump units or the electric resistance heating, motor-driven cooling combinations are frequently remotely located and connected to the various air conditioning areas

111

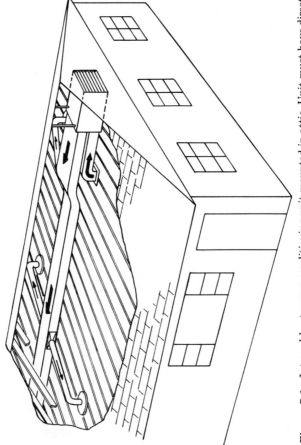

Figure 7-1 Integral heat pump conditioning unit mounted in attic. Unit must have direct access to outdoor air.

by means of supply and return ducts. The essential working parts of a central plant unit include blower, heating and cooling surfaces, air filters, and controls. The blower circulates the air through the conditioner and duct system against the resistance imposed by the system. Integral conditioner units (Figure 7-1) also contain the refrigeration compressor and the air-cooled condenser. In contrast, the compressor and condenser compartment for the split type design is located on the exterior of the structure, as shown in Figures 7-2 and 7-3.

Many heat pump units and electric heating-cooling combination units are small, attractive and quiet enough to be located anywhere desired, for example, in a basement recreation room, a closet or alcove adjacent to the living quarters, a utility room, or an attic. Special horizontal models are available to fit easily into an unfurnished attic or below the basement ceiling. The section housing the compressor can be located in the roof gable (Figure 7-1) or outside of the house as shown by Figures 7-2 and 7-3. The indoor conditioner unit rests on ceiling joists, or, if a basement installation, it can hang from the basement ceiling joists or can be supported from the side walls.

The forced air distribution system extends from the centrally located unit to various rooms in the house. The ducts, volume dampers, return air intakes, and supply air outlets comprise the duct system. The duct system returns the air from the room to the unit and supplies either heated or cooled, filtered, conditioned air from the unit to the room. Ventilation air may also be introduced to the space through the duct system. If the conditioner unit is located in

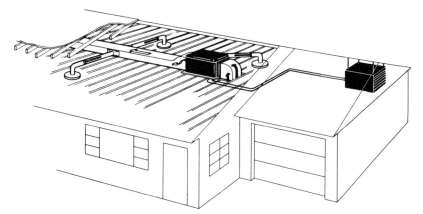

Figure 7-2 Air-to-air, split type heat pump. Conditioner unit is located in the attic space, and outdoor section installed in garage.

Figure 7-3   Outdoor section of a split type, air-to-air heat pump can be mounted on a ground slab. Section contains compressor, air-refrigerant transfer surface, and accessories.

a nonconditioned space, such as an attic or basement, it is vital to insulate both the equipment and the ductwork so that the cool air in summer and the warm air in winter are not lost to outside the conditioned space.

Duct Systems   The design of the duct system is influenced by the types of construction, the location of the conditioner units, the type of air circulation desired within the room, and by the location of supply and return grilles. The recommended size of the ducts and the permissible velocities, together with the proper selection procedure, may be found in the *ASHRAE Guide* or in a good air conditioning textbook. Ducts, either round or rectangular in cross section, must be permanent, rigid, nonbuckling, nonrattling, and have airtight joints. Galvanized iron, aluminum, or prefabricated nonmetallic ducts are acceptable.

The design of the duct system plays an important part in the first cost and in the general satisfaction and acceptance of an installation. The three basic types of duct systems applicable to residential year-round heating and cooling installations are:

1. the box plenum with individual take-off
2. the extended plenum duct system
3. the trunk duct system

The *box plenum arrangement* can generally be used in connection with perimeter radial systems or with perimeter loop systems having low, outside wall supply grilles and central returns, as shown in Figures 7-4 and 7-5. This type of duct system has certain advantages where it is possible to construct a box plenum. In this arrangement, air from the central box is supplied to the space by means of a number of individual ducts with butt take-off connection. The duct plenum can be located above the floor in a utility room or below the floor in a basement or crawl space. The ducts can be located in a basement, in a crawl space, or in the floor slab. The perimeter radial system consists of individual ducts running spokewise below the floor, from the plenum to each perimeter outlet. Each branch duct delivers a controlled volume of conditioned air. Edge insulation is essential for the floor slab and crawl space systems, and the proper amount of duct insulation with the proper vapor barrier must be used on supply and return ducts in nonconditioned spaces. With slab construction, the ducts may be cast directly in the slab, or concrete channels may be formed in the slab during the pouring. In cold climates, this type of distribution has the advantage of warming the floor in the winter but the heat losses to the ground may be increased.

For homes without basements the so-called perimeter system, constructed in concrete slabs or crawl spaces, normally uses single-size diameter piping on all runs to distribute the conditioned air to the supply grilles. In cases where the heating and cooling requirements exceed the carrying capacity of the standard duct, the pipes and grilles are maintained at the same size, but additional runs are made. The individual duct system is easy to install and balance and gives better air distribution within the room. In many cases, however, this design may prove fairly expensive if a large number of individual elongated ducts are to be run to a far end of a building.

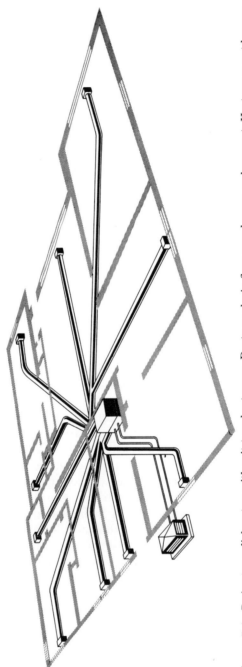

Figure 7-4 Perimeter radial system with spit-type heat pump. Ducts can be in floor, crawl space, or basement. Heat pump outdoor section can be on ground slab, and indoor section on utility room floor or ceiling.

116

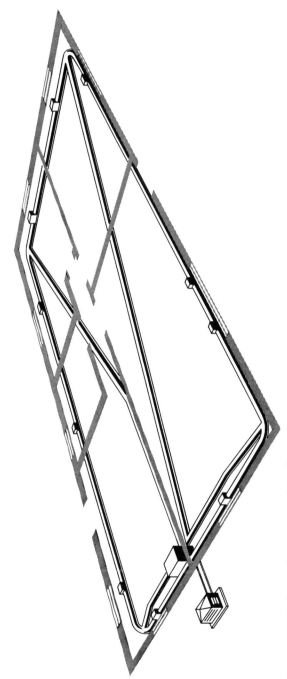

Figure 7-5 Perimeter loop system with split-type heat pump. Ducts can be in floor, crawl space, or basement. Heat pump outdoor section can be on ground slab, and indoor section in utility room or basement.

Furthermore, the heat loss from the ducts can be large and the duct transmission efficiency low.

The *extended plenum* is used extensively for residential installations. In this arrangement, as shown in Figure 7-6, the trunk duct is not reduced in cross section. A number of branch ducts connected to the extended plenum with simple branch take-off connections are in turn connected to the supply grilles. The extended plenum can be used with perimeter radial or perimeter loop systems (located in basement or crawl space) and with ceiling and high sidewall installations as shown in Figures 7-7 and 7-8. The static air pressure and the air flow in an extended plenum duct system tend to be constant throughout the length of the duct. In small installations, where the cost of the additional sheet metal is of little consequence compared to saving in installation labor and fabrication, the extended plenum system has proven very practical.

The *trunk duct system* differs from the extended plenum in that the cross section decreases after each take-off, in order to keep a constant static pressure drop per length of duct. This type of duct system is practical for the larger installations, where considerable amount of ductwork is involved.

Each of the three basic types of forced air distribution systems, illustrated in Figures 7-4 through 7-8, requires certain accessories such as volume dampers, supply air outlets and return air intakes to regulate the flow of air to the conditioned space. The design and selection of these accessories are very important to the maintaining of satisfactory indoor comfort at all outdoor temperatures.

Volume dampers are generally an integral part of the outlet grille or else are located in the supply ducts immediately adjacent to the outlets. In systems with more than one return air inlet, volume dampers are also frequently installed in the return ductwork. These dampers regulate the quantity of air flowing through the various ducts and are used to balance the system.

Grilles, registers, and diffusers require careful consideration. Supply grilles should be located so as to direct the air toward the areas having the greatest heat loss and heat gain. They can be located in the floor, the baseboard, above the baseboard, high in the sidewall, or in the ceiling. Low sidewall and baseboard grilles should be located to be particularly effective in counteracting currents of cool or hot air due to exposed walls or leakage from doors or windows; possible interference with furniture placement and draperies must be considered.

The supplies and returns are manufactured in many sizes for a

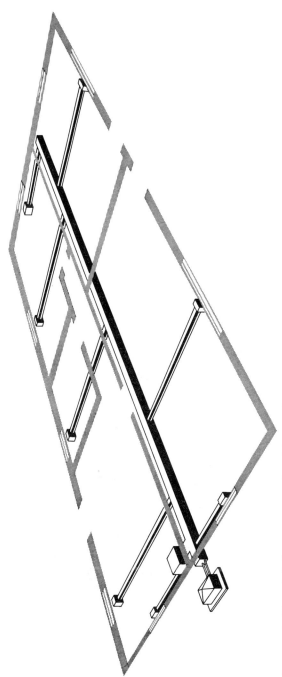

Figure 7-6 Extended plenum connected to either a split-type or an integral heat pump. Trunk duct, with uniform cross section, can be located in crawl space or basement.

119

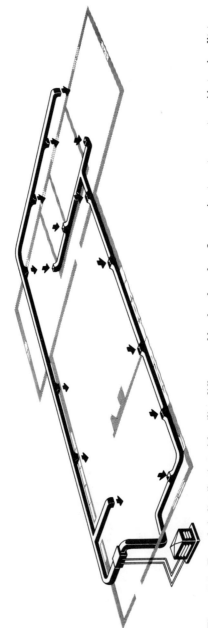

Figure 7-7 Forced air distribution with ceiling diffusers and low baseboard, or floor, perimeter return system. Air-to-air split-type or integral heat pump furnishes the year-round air conditioning.

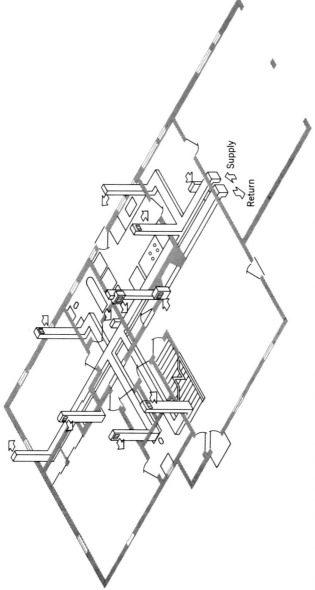

Supply
Return

Figure 7-8 High sidewall, forced air distribution system with two central, inside wall returns. Can be used with a split or integral heat pump.

variety of applications. The size of the grilles are determined from the design consideration of the system and the heating and cooling loads. The type depends upon the system being used and its location in the room.

Changes in the type, velocity, and location of the supply grilles affect the room conditions much more than changes in location of the returns. It has been found that if the supplies are selected so that a small difference in floor to ceiling temperature exists the locations of the return registers have no significant effect on the comfort conditions. In fact, contrary to popular belief, room air cannot be pulled toward a return grille. The suction effect of a return grille is limited to the immediate vicinity. Even with a velocity of 1000 fpm at the opening (which is seldom, if ever, used) the flow toward the grille is only 25 fpm at a distance of 2 ft. The only precaution necessary is to prevent short circuiting between the supply and return and to prevent locating the grille near seated occupants, because of possible air movement and noise. With a properly selected and located supply grille, therefore, it is unnecessary to have a return duct from each room; instead, the hallway can be used as a return, either by undercutting the doors or by installing grilles in doors or partition walls.

If heating is of major or equal importance, perimeter floor supply diffusers have been found to be best, followed by floor registers, high sidewall, and ceiling diffusers in that order. If cooling is to be the primary application and heating is of secondary importance, because of relatively mild outdoor design conditions, ceiling diffusers will perform the most satisfactorily. It has been found that with ceiling diffusers the room temperature variation is almost negligible during the cooling cycle, regardless of supply velocity. High sidewall registers are next in satisfaction when cooling is the basic requirement, followed by floor registers.

Perimeter diffusers are usually designed for use in specific locations and with special types of systems to direct the air upward in a fan-shaped pattern. They can be located in the floor near the outside wall or in the outside wall, in or just above the baseboard and preferably under the window. Floor outlets may detract from appearance and can cause a dirty surface. There should be a sufficient number of outlets in each room so that all exposed surfaces are blanketed with a curtain of air. The supply air should be delivered with sufficient upward velocity to eliminate stratification of hot or cold air (depending on the cycle) near the floor. The minimum, recommended supply velocity for a floor diffuser is 500 fpm, but 600 to

700 fpm results in a better air pattern. Lower velocities are insufficient to project cool air to ceiling and cause it to spread, but instead allow the cool air to drop to the floor and create cold areas.

Floor supply diffusers, of all the outlets, are the most dependent upon air velocity, with floor registers a close second. It has been found however that floor registers with vertical nonspreading air jets can produce comfortable conditions. These floor type grilles may also detract from the appearance of a room and can cause wall discoloration.

High sidewall registers should be of the type that will deliver the air horizontally or in a slightly downward direction and should be so located as to avoid direct impingement of air on ceiling or walls. The air velocity through the register, however, should be sufficient to prevent cold air, during the cooling cycle, from dropping into the occupied space and causing uncomfortable air motion or drafts. Directional type registers should be used for the best results.

Ceiling diffusers are used in both residential and commercial applications. It is important to have the proper design and size of outlet so that the air will not be reflected from the walls of the room to cause uncomfortable conditions when the required volume is delivered. Ceiling diffusers should be used with caution, during the heating cycle, in those areas where below-freezing temperatures occur frequently and where warm floors are of prime consideration, unless the floors, as well as walls, windows, and doors, have the recommended insulation.

Other components affecting the operation and satisfaction of a system include controls, air filters, and thermal insulation. Controls should be automatic to coordinate properly the functions of all components of year-round air conditioning systems. To regulate the indoor air temperature thermostats should be located at about a 30-in. level within the occupied space. The location should be unaffected by heat from an outside source, such as sun through the windows, radiation effect of fireplaces, supply outlets, and heat-producing appliances. Other controls are essential to safe and economical operation, as covered by Chapter 4.

Air filters are also an essential part of a conditioner system. This air-cleaning and purification equipment removes lint, dirt, soot, pollen, smoke, and other foreign matter from the air circulated through the structure. Many filters consist of fibrous materials, such as bonded glass fibers, aluminum hair, or treated papers tightly packed between meshed or woven material. Many filters trap or entrain most of the larger particles, but have little effect in stopping the smaller particles. Much better filtration than that generally used can often be economically justified, as described in Chapter 6.

Thermal insulation of the structure is a major contributing factor to the satisfactory operation of any heating and cooling distribution system. With the proper amount of wall and ceiling insulation and by the use of good storm windows and doors, the inside surface temperature will more closely approach the air temperature. This warmer indoor surface temperature, together with the reduction of the infiltration air, affords more freedom in the selection and location of the supply grilles, as well as in the quantity of air to be conditioned. This very important subject is more fully discussed in Chapter 6.

Hydronic Systems Residences. In a hydronic system, warm or chilled water is circulated through a closed piping system containing heating-cooling surfaces, circulating pumps, expansion tanks, and connecting piping as shown in Figure 7-9.

During the heating cycle, the warm water is circulated through the conditioner coils (connected to the ductwork) or the convectors (located directly in the room) which in turn transfer the heat to the ambient air. Similarly, during the cooling cycle, cold water is circulated through the same or similar surfaces to reduce the air temperature and to remove the unwanted humidity. The connecting water pipes must be insulated to prevent condensation on the exposed surfaces during the cooling cycle and to prevent waste of both cooling and heating to the nonconditioned spaces.

The convectors, located directly in the room, must be equipped with a fan, heat transfer coils, and air filters, as in the larger central plant units. Such convectors are particularly attractive for air-to-water heat pump service to provide circulation, cooling, heating, and filtering of the room air. The paramount advantages of the hydronic system are flexibility and zoning possibilities. The convectors can easily be operated individually to permit separate temperature control in each room. This system is particularly attractive both for the older, existing homes when summer air conditioning is to be added and for the larger new homes where it is frequently rather difficult to install the larger, more cumbersome ductwork. In many instances the hydronic equipment is comparatively higher in first cost, but because of its inherent flexibility and simplicity may frequently have a lower total owning and operating cost.

The hydronic system can quite readily be combined with the domestic hot water system and with off-peak storage systems (see Chapter 2). The maximum electric demand of the heat pump and re-

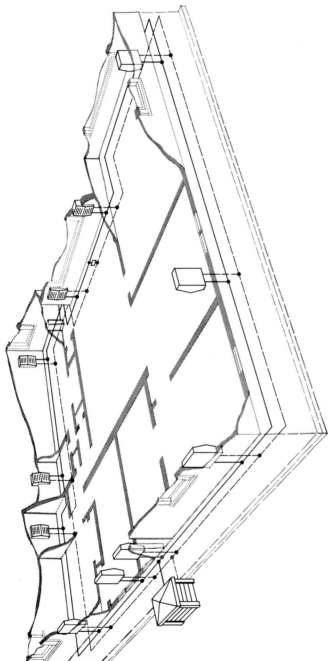

Figure 7-9 Hydronic warm and chilled water system with individual fan-coil room units. An integral air-to-water heat pump is used for heating and cooling.

125

sistance heating at the extreme outdoor temperatures will usually coincide with the daytime peak demand of the other electrical equipment. To minimize this electric demand some of the utilities offer incentive rates to encourage recharging of the storage tanks during the specified periods when excess electric generation capacity is available. The heat and cold from storage can then be used during the prescribed daytime period and thereby take full advantage of the off-peak demand rates.

Individual Self-Contained Room Units. A particularly attractive method of year-round air conditioning is to use small, self-contained, integral units for individual room conditioning.

Through-the-wall units can be installed directly in the exterior walls of the structure, as illustrated in Figure 7-10. Such installations have the advantage over the more common window units of not taking valuable window space.

The self-contained integral units may be either heat pumps with or without supplemental resistance heat or mechanical cooling units with resistance heat. They consist of the heating and cooling surfaces, refrigerating compressors, controls, and power wiring, so arranged and interconnected to make a complete system. These individual, in-the-room type, units, where applicable, possess many inherent advantages in flexibility and lower first cost over the central plant type of equipment. These advantages are equally applicable to residential, commercial, and industrial application.

COMMERCIAL AND INDUSTRIAL SYSTEMS

Any of the generally accepted, year-round air conditioning distribution systems can be used for heat pumps or for the electric heat motor-driven cooling equipment combination.

For the multi-story office building, either the high-air velocity induction system (as illustrated in Figure 7-11) or fan-coil units (Figure 7-12), or the integral, self-contained, in-the-wall type of unit (Figure 7-10) can be used.

The high-air velocity induction system is a combination, forced air hydronic system. The primary air is supplied to the perimeter unit under high pressure and velocity. Fans are unnecessary in this type of system since the high velocity primary air circulates room air over the heating or cooling coil in each unit by induction. This primary air and water is remotely preheated or precooled, depending on the cycle, before it is circulated through the room unit as shown in Figure 7-11. A number of equipment combinations are possible, depending upon the zoning and other requirements. Simultaneous

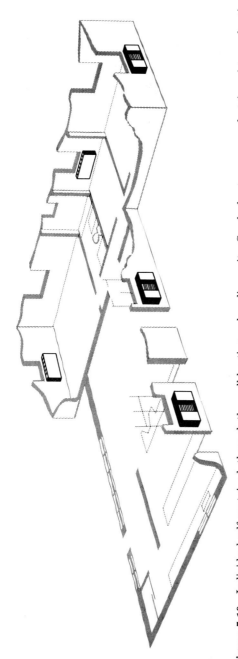

Figure 7-10 Individual self-contained, through-the-wall heating and cooling units. Can be heat pumps or electric resistance heating, motor-driven cooling units.

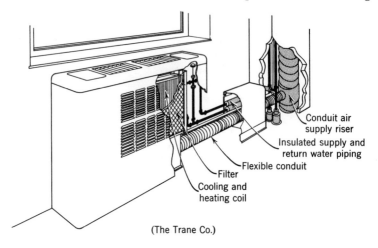

(The Trane Co.)

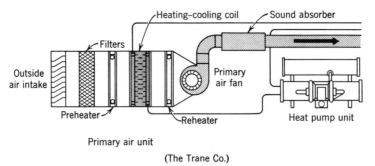

Figure 7-11 High-velocity, perimeter induction system, for multi-story office building. Primary air unit and warm and chilled water system are connected to a central station air-to-water or water-to-water heat pump.

heating and cooling by the different centrally located equipment, by means of either a 3- or 4-pipe system, are possible, although in most cases rather costly. Coils and/or lint screens on these induction units require periodic maintenance with a vacuum cleaner which can be a rather costly operation.

The design and application of fan-coil units are similar to those described for the induction units. The main difference is that fans and fan motors are located within the room units. Basically, the fan-coil unit is a small air conditioning unit that consists of one or more fans, fan motor, cooling and heating coils, filter, controls, and decorative housing. Any of the acceptable hydronic heating and cooling systems, such as shown in Figure 7-12, is satisfactory for this type of application.

Ventilation air for the space served by the fan-coil units can be supplied through an opening in the exterior wall of the building at each unit, or from an exterior zone where the correct quantity of supply air is introduced into the space. Preconditioned ventilation air can also be supplied to each area served by a fan-coil unit through a separate duct system similar to that followed for induction units.

Application advantages in a fan-coil installation include independent temperatures, air circulation, filtering, ventilation, and humidities which can usually be provided at a considerable saving in cost over other comparable installations. The system is very flexible, since each unit can operate independently of the other and requires a minimum amount of engineering, installation, and maintenance. The

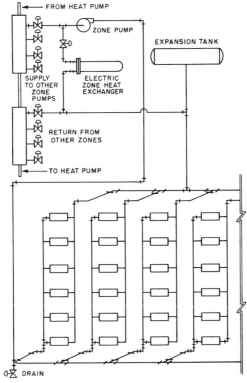

Figure 7-12 Fan-coil, warm and chilled water, year-round air conditioning system. For multi-story office building. Can be a two-pipe system (as shown), a three-pipe, or four-pipe, connected to a central station air-to-water or water-to-water heat pump.

unit, however, must be selected with care to prevent objectionable noise transmission. The units are generally equipped with a multi-speed fan switch to permit the lower operating speeds that provide sufficient heating and cooling for the majority of the time.

The individual, integral, self-contained, in-the-wall type of heating and cooling unit is also applicable to commercial and industrial installations, such as motels, multi-story apartments, or the peripheral areas of office buildings. These kinds of installations are equally applicable to new and to existing buildings.

The heat pump or electric resistance heating-cooling equipment for the commercial and industrial installations can be located on the roof, in between floors, in the basement, or in many other places. For a one-story building, such as shopping centers or similar types of structure the roof-mounted application, as shown by items 1 and 2 of Figure 7-13, has considerable appeal. The equipment for 1 is enclosed in a penthouse whereas 2 is exposed to the weather. Item 3 of Figure 7-13 can be a self-contained unit or can be the outdoor section of a split unit. In this case, the outdoor section could be represented by item 4 for a ground installation, or this section can also be placed in the basement or on the roof. Item 5 on this figure represents a self-contained heating and cooling installation at ground level. Any of these units can supply the heating and cooling effect either by means of a forced air duct system as shown or by means of a hydronic system, whichever is more practical.

Outdoor Air Intakes. These are usually provided as part of a forced air system to introduce outdoor ventilation air into a structure. This outdoor air is conveyed through an individual duct leading from the outdoors directly to the return plenum of the conditioner unit and should be provided with either manual or automatic-operated dampers. The introduction of large quantities of outdoor air into a structure will result in increased operating cost and make the control of the humidity in the structure more difficult. The desire for maintaining positive pressure within the building is sometimes given as the reason for the ventilation air quantities. In general, even with moderately large amounts of outdoor air introduced into a structure, it is not possible to maintain indoor pressure sufficiently to stop window infiltration. It must be realized that door and window crackage and other such openings permit air to flow readily from the structure to the outdoors directly in proportion to the pressure created. The use of carbon and electric filters to reduce the ventilation air requirements and the corresponding owning and operating costs are described in Chapter 6.

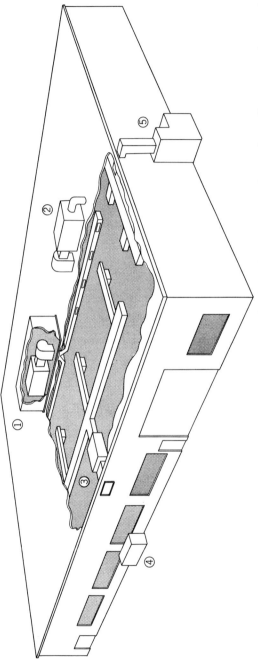

Figure 7-13 Typical air-to-air heat pump systems for commercial and industrial structures. 1. Integral or split-type, penthouse unit. 2. Integral roof-type unit. 3. Integral unit or indoor section of a split-type. 4. Outdoor section of split unit. 5. Ground level installation. Can be any one of several different designs.

131

REFERENCES

ASHRAE Guide and Data Book, Fundamentals and Equipment, Chap. 47, Air-Diffusing
Equipment, 1965.

Divine, William H., Fan Coil Units and Systems, *Air Conditioning, Heating and Ventilating,* December 1959.

Konzo, S., Warm Air Heating, *Air Conditioning, Heating and Ventilating,* Reference
Section, October 1955.

Selection of Distribution System, Manual 6, National Warm Air Heating and Air Conditioning Association, 1963.

Wright, J. Richard, Comparative Performance of Systems Used for Year-Round Air
Conditioning of Research Residence 2, *ASHRAE Journal,* November 1963.

Wright, J. Richard, D. R. Bahnfleth, and E. J. Brown, Comparative Performance of
Year-Round Systems Used in Air Conditioning Research Residence No. 2, *Univer-
sity of Illinois Engineering Experiment Station Bulletin 465,* 1963.

Chapter 8

Economics of the Electric Heating Concept: *Effect on the Power System Load Curve*

The cost to the electric utility company of supplying service to a customer is directly related to the diversified annual load factor as illustrated by Figure 8-1. This hyperbolic curve indicates that the cost of service varies inversely with the diversified annual load factor. The cost-to-serve factor includes the cost of the energy and demand components, as well as the cost of facilities, including the generation plant, for transmitting and distributing the power to the customer's premises. The diversified annual load factors are based on maximum coincident demands at the time of system peak during the coldest week.

The cost-load factor relationship may vary somewhat, depending on the geographic location and various operating conditions, but the general shape of the curve should not change materially. A 49 percent load factor was assumed for the 100 percent reference point because it is representative of the value generally obtained by the present-day residential customer with light, appliances, and domestic water heating but no space heating and cooling. It is to be noted from Figure 8-1 that a minimum diversified load factor in the neighborhood of 30 percent is desirable, and the cost per kilowatt-hour increases very rapidly below this point.

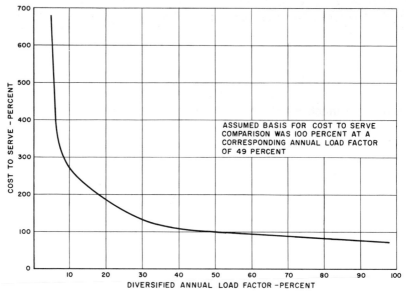

Figure 8-1 The relation between the diversified annual load factor and the cost to serve an electric customer.

RESIDENTIAL ELECTRIC SPACE HEATING LOAD CHARACTERISTICS (*Resistance Heating*)

Many field observations and tests have been made by various electric utilities, to obtain a reasonably accurate determination of the diversified demand and load characteristics of electrically heated residences. Out of these available data were drawn typical load curves for a group of houses, depicted in Figures 8-2 through 8-7, for an area experiencing 4500 to 6000 degree days. These load curves are based on a 30-min, integrated demand period. In any evaluation it is important to use the same demand period, since the integrated demand for a given load decreases as the time period increases. For instance, about a 35 percent decrease has been observed in the increase between a 15-min to a 30-min integrated heating demand, and another decrease of about 4 percent is realized between a 30-min demand to an hourly demand. For a nonheating load the 30-min demand is about 2½ percent higher than the 60-min demand.

The shape and magnitude of the energy consumption, diversified demand, and load factor curves of electric space heating installations may also vary considerably, depending upon the extent and type of utilization devices installed, family living habits, weather conditions, geographic location, type of structures, amount of thermal insulation, heat storage effect of the structure, the type, size, and basic design of the system. Another important consideration is the type of operating cycle employed. Maintaining a uniform indoor temperature throughout the 24 hours of the day, for example, will result in a much more attractive load curve than that obtained by lowering the temperature at night. When night setback is employed, the size of the heating equipment must be increased as much as 25 to 40 percent to provide means of quickly restoring the heat, especially on cold days. The lower ambient temperature together with the larger heaters causes a high pickup load during the early morning hours, with little or no diversity.

Therefore, such load characteristic curves as shown in these figures can only be representative and cannot be safely used to determine the actual characteristics of other groups, unless they are similar in all respects. Figure 8-2 shows the expected daily maximum diversified demand of the total load and the resistance heating load for a group of about 35 all-electric residential customers during the coldest day of the year. The temperature during the day ranged between -10 F and $+10$ F with an average of 0 F.

Starting in the early morning hours, the average diversified heating demand per customer rose slowly to reach a peak at 5:30 A.M. and then gradually decreased for the next three hours. At 8:30 A.M. the heating demand dropped sharply and continued downward until about 12:30 P.M. At 4 P.M. the heating demand started a steady climb which continued during the night to repeat the cycle the next day.

It can be noted that the frequency and duration of the heating demand is governed principally by the change in heating degree hours. The demand rose during the night as the degree hours increased (outdoor temperature dropped) and conversely dropped during the day as the degree hours decreased (outdoor temperature increased).

The average total diversified daily demand of the group of electrically heated houses, as shown in Figure 8-2, is closely related to the heating load because of the predominance of the heating load. Starting in the morning at 5:30 A.M. the total demand increases sharply by 1.2 kw and remains at a high level for the next three hours, because of the living habits of the occupants, even though the heating load decreased. At 8:30 A.M. the total load also drops sharply and stays reasonably constant, except for a small rise of

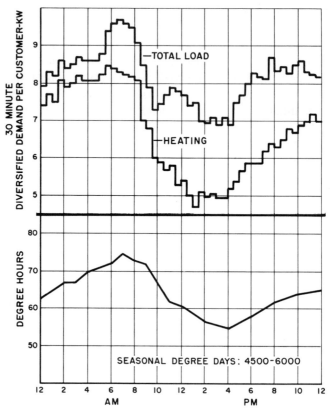

Figure 8-2 Typical 30-minute maximum diversified demand curves of the total load and heating load for a group of 35 all-electric residential customers on the coldest day during the coldest week.

0.5 kw around noon. At 4 P.M. the total demand parallels the rise in the heating load until the 7 to 8 P.M. evening peak is reached. From this peak the load gradually decreases during the night.

Figure 8-3 shows typical maximum diversified demand curves of the total and resistance heating loads for the same group of all-electric houses on an average day during the coldest week. On this day the temperature varied from 5 F to 25 F with an average of 15 F. The heating demand of this warmer day follows the outdoor temperature variation in a manner similar to that experienced on the colder day covered by Figure 8-2. The total demand also parallels the heating demand, except for the 7 to 8 A.M. morning and 6 to 7:30 P.M. evening peaks which are caused by the preparation of meals and other living habits of the occupants.

It can be noted that the maximum coincident total and heating demands of 9.7 and 8.5 kw for the average 0 F day were reduced to 8.6 and 6.9 kw respectively for the 15 F day. The maximum total diversified demand of the other appliances (total demand minus the heating), for the 15 F day, ranges from 0.6 and 1.9 kw with the evening peak having the highest value. The demand of the other appliances load is independent of the size of the heating demands and the corresponding outdoor temperatures.

The heating demand during the day is usually lower than at night, for a given outdoor temperature, because of the effect of the heat gain (internal and solar) on the heating requirements. The effect of the useful internal and solar gain on the diversified kw heating demand is indicated in Figure 8-4. For this particular group of

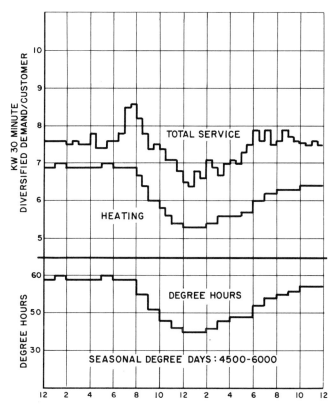

Figure 8-3 Typical 30-minute maximum diversified demand curves of the total service and heating load for a group of about 35 all-electric residential customers for an average day during coldest week.

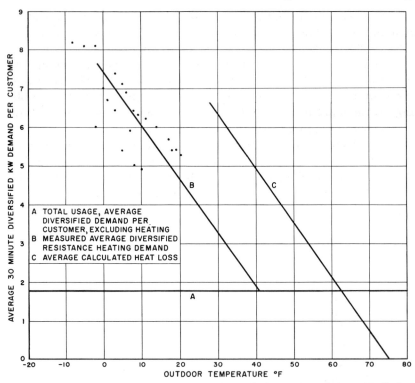

Figure 8-4 Average 30-minute diversified demands for a group of about 35 all-electric residences at various outdoor temperatures during coldest week.

houses, during the coldest week, the internal and solar gain accounted for an average 3 kw demand, which represents a sizable reduction in the heating requirements. Full consideration of this internal heat gain is very important in evaluating the total demand at the time of system peak and in determining the resulting kwh for the period.

The average electric energy consumption of appliances per household per year has increased from about 2400 kwhr in 1953 to 4500 kwhr in 1963. In electrically heated homes this average figure can reach 7600 kwhr. This increase in electric energy usage, together with a greater density of living habits per unit of residential floor area and the higher standards of thermal insulation, is causing the heat gain to be a larger and larger contributing factor to the structure heat loss. Several studies on groups of all-electric residences have indicated that this internal and solar gain has contributed up to 35 percent of the total annual heating requirements.

The residential groups, covered by Figures 8-2, 8-3, and 8-4, have a relatively high-percent saturation of electric appliances. The type of appliance and the percent saturation are given in Table 8-1 for the group of 35 houses with resistance heating and heat pumps. Some of the other important operating characteristics of the group of all-electric homes, for the day with the maximum diversified heating demand, are also given in the tabulation. The coincident factor of the heating load component of this group is higher than for the total. Consequently, the annual load factor of the heating load is lower than that of the total load. Unquestionably, the heating load is dominant in the case of the resistance heated house, since it represents about 60 percent of the total annual energy consumption and accounts for about 87 percent of the total demand at the time of the morning peak. The average, total load, annual load factor of a group based on maximum diversified demand is usually 28 to 36 percent and may increase to a range of 33 to 40 percent when the summer cooling load is added. In contrast, the average, diversified, monthly load factor ranges between 45 to 50 percent. There are many who believe that the monthly load factor approach is more realistic and should be used in comparing the relative merits of the two types of loads. Also, lower load factors than normal may be attractive for electric heating because of the ability of the distribution transformers to operate at 200 percent of rated capacity at peak load, which generally occurs at minimum outdoor temperatures.

The maximum diversified demand of the heating and total loads for the coldest day influences the sizing and selection of the secondary power transmission and distribution system, but the coincident demand at the time of the system peak is the important component in any cost-to-serve determination. Electric utility system load curves vary considerably, depending upon the type of load served and the geographic location. A typical curve, on the day of maximum demand, for a large utility system is given in Figure 8-5. This shows that the 11 A.M. morning peak is about equal to the 6 P.M. evening peak. If a group of electrically heated residences, as given in Figure 8-2, is superimposed on the system load curve, the coincident heating and total loads at the time of morning peak are 5.8 and 7.9 kw and at the time of evening peak 5.9 and 8.2 kw. The all-important diversified demand at the time of evening system peak, which is the largest in this particular instance, results in a coincident factor of 57 percent for heating and 65 percent for total service. Actually, it has been found in most cases where resistance heating installations are properly engineered and thermostatically controlled that the coinci-

TABLE 8-1   Load Characteristics and Other Data for a Group of Thirty-five All-electric Homes on Day of Maximum Demand During Coldest Week, Average per Customer

Operating Characteristics	Resistance Heating	Heat Pumps
1. Load, connected, kw		
Heating	13.0	10.4
Total		
2. Demand, maximum noncoincident, kw		
Heating	10.4	7.8
Total	12.5	9.9
3. Demand, 30-min maximum diversified, kw		
Heating	8.5	6.8
Total	9.7	8.0
4. Coincident factor, %		
Heating	81.6	87.1
Total	77.6	80.8
5. Load factor, annual, %		
(a) Based on maximum diversified demand		
Heating	20.2	10.3
Total	29.7	23.4
(b) Based on maximum noncoincident demand		
Heating	16.5	9.0
Total	23.0	18.9
6. Degree days (65 F base), heating season	5,750	5,750
7. Kilowatthours, annual		
Heating	15,000	5,350
Cooling	2,600	2,600
Fan, indoor conditioner	50	830
General service	7,600	7,600
Total	25,250	16,380

Appliances	Customer Saturation, %
Ranges	100
Water heaters, uncontrolled	100
Refrigerators	100
Freezers	15
Automatic clothes dryers	70
Dishwashers	25
Summer air conditioning	100
Television	95

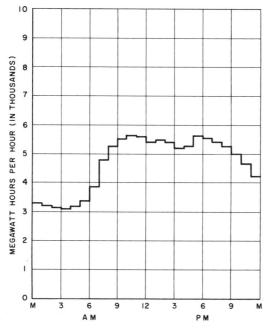

Figure 8-5   System 60-minute integrated demand curve of a large electric utility system on the day of maximum demand.

dent factor at the times of the maximum system peak ranges between 45 and 65 percent.

It has been shown that a definite relationship exists for a group of all-electric residences between the heating kilowatthours, the total load kilowatthours, and daily degree hours or outdoor temperatures. This same relationship exists on a monthly basis, as shown in Figure 8-6. It is to be noted that such a direct relationship does not usually exist for individual residential installations. Instead, the noncoincident maximum demand of individual customers with the same connected load, under a given set of conditions, may vary as much as 25 to 100 percent, with a corresponding increase in kilowatthours. The maximum demand of a particular individual customer does not necessarily occur on the coldest day; in fact, it has been observed to take place over a wide range of time in almost any winter month from November through March. A peak demand which occurs late in the heating season is usually caused by resetting the thermostat during the night setting and is not related to the outdoor temperature. There are many seasonal variations which will affect the maximum demand and the kilowatt consumption, such as the

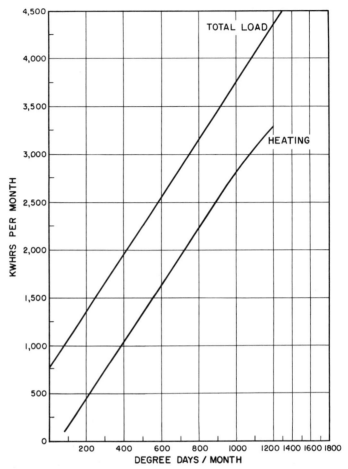

Figure 8-6 Relationship between average kilowatthours and degree days for group of about 35 typical all-electric residences in area with 5750 degree days per year. Average connected demand and percent saturation of appliances given in Table 8-1.

length of the day, inlet water temperature fluctuation for domestic water heating, a house temperature not maintained at the same level on cold and warm days, and finally, the heating load during falling temperature is different from that during rising temperature. High winds increase heat losses to produce a higher heating demand for a given outdoor temperature. As the residences are grouped together, the individual characteristics tend to disappear so that the averaged diversified demand and the kilowatthours for a group of 35 or more residences will have both a definite relationship to the outdoor temperature and resulting degree days for a reasonably long period of time, such as a week, month, or season.

The average monthly heating, cooling, and total kilowatthours for the group of residential customers together with the corresponding degree days are shown in Figure 8-7. This figure again shows that the most important single factor of the many variables which in-

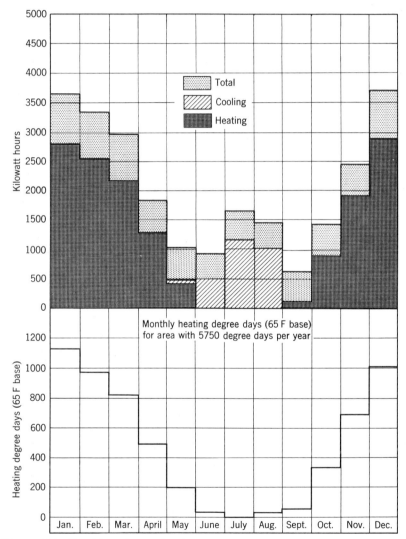

Figure 8-7   Monthly resistance heating, cooling and total kilowatthours for average residence with design characteristics as given in Table 8-1.

fluence the heating kilowatthour is the outdoor temperature or the corresponding heating degree days. It is to be noted that heating is required during the 9 months of the year, and cooling is used for only 4 months by this group of residences in this geographic area. The annual average heating kilowatthours are 15,000, the cooling kilowatthours are 2600, for a total of 17,600 kwhr.

RESIDENTIAL ELECTRIC SPACE HEATING LOAD CHARACTERISTICS (*Heat Pumps*)

Heat pump load characteristics curves are similar to the resistance heating curves shown in Figures 8-2 and 8-3. There is little difference in the shape of the curves or the diversity with the other electrical uses. The average 30-min diversified kilowatt demand per customer for a group of heat pumps, however, may be quite different from that for a group of resistance heating customers, depending on the heat pump balance point, with structure heat loss, and on the coefficient of performance or performance factor of the equipment.

The average operating characteristics of the probable heat pump selection for the same group of residences (used to demonstrate the resistance heating performance) are given in Figure 8-8. The heat pump heating output decreases with outdoor temperature so that the estimated balance point (outdoor temperature with output equalling calculated heat loss, curve *D*) is 25½ F. The balance point, when corrected for the useful internal and solar gain, which is the correct one to use in load studies, is 9 F for the average group of residences under consideration. With such a balance point and with an outdoor design temperature of 0 F, the heat pump would furnish 17,000 Btuh of the 25,500 required, and resistance heat would supply the remainder. In this case the average diversified demand per customer of the heat pump plus the resistance heating (2.4 + 2.5) is 4.9 kw. At −10 F outdoor design temperature, this proportion would change so that the heat pump demand would be 2.2 and resistance heating would increase to 5.3, for a total of 7.5 kw.

Based on the heat pump performance given in Figure 8-8, the expected 30-min average diversified demand per customer for the coldest day of the year is given in Figure 8-9. The load curve is based on the same operating conditions and the same type and kind of residences used in Figure 8-2, for the group of resistance heating customers. The average diversified heating demand per customer with heat pumps ranges from the maximum of 7.5 at 7 A.M. to the minimum of 2.4 at 4 P.M. The comparable values for resistance heating is 8.5 and 4.9 kw respectively. The average maximum diversified of

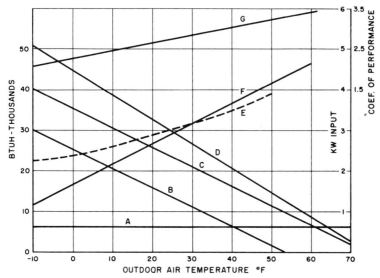

Figure 8-8 Curve showing relationship between heat pump performance and structure heat loss at various outdoor temperatures for a group of about 35 all-electric residences.
(A) Btuh equiv. to average total diversified demand per customer, excluding heating. (B) Btuh heat loss-equiv. to average kw diversified resistance heating demand per customer. (C) Btuh heat loss-equiv. to average kw noncoincident resistance heating demand per customer. (D) Btuh calculated heat loss-average per customer. (E) Kw input-heat pump (compressor & outdoor air fans). (F) Btuh heating output of heat pump—no supplemental resistance heat. (G) Coefficient of performance of heat pump.

the total load is, therefore, 8.7 for the heat pump residences and 9.7 for the resistance heating structures. This difference is limited to 1 kw because the heat pump is assisted by supplemental resistance heat during the coldest part of the day. The warmer part of the day, however, is much more favorable to the heat pump since the difference in demand between the two systems is about 2.0 kw.

The most attractive feature of heat pumps in comparison to resistance heating, however, is the possible reduction in the kilowatt-hours. The estimated, average heating energy consumption for a 0 F day, as illustrated by Figure 8-9 for example, is 160 kwhr for the resistance-heated house as compared with 116 kwhr for the heat pump house, of which over half is consumed by the supplemental heaters. On an annual basis, the possible savings on the energy consumption with the heat pump is even more attractive. As shown by Table 8-1 this saving can amount to an average of 8870 kwhr per year for each of the houses in the group.

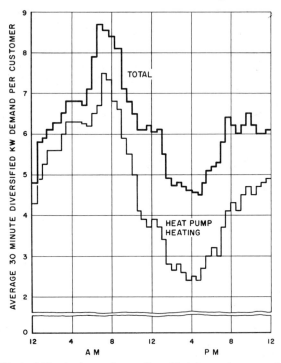

Figure 8-9 Typical 30-minute maximum diversified demand curves of the total load and heat pump heating load for a group of about 35 all-electric residential customers on the coldest day, during the coldest week of the year.

The main objection frequently cited against the heat pump is the low annual load factor caused by the supplemental resistance heat. As shown in Figure 8-9, the supplemental resistance heating can materially raise the average maximum diversified demand with a corresponding decrease in the annual load factor, if based on the maximum diversified demand for the coldest day of the year. As stated in connection with the discussion of resistance heating there are many utilities, of the opinion that the annual load factors based on average monthly demand are more realistic, because maximum demands caused by the extreme temperatures are very infrequent and are of short duration. Also, the coincident factor at the time of system peak, which will generally occur during the day when a minimum amount of supplement heat is being used, is a most important consideration. On this basis, the heat pump annual load factor is about the same as for resistance heat.

The possibilities of reducing the maximum coincident demand of a residence by limiting the operation of a particular appliance has frequently been cited. The lighting, miscellaneous appliances, ranges, and water heating have a maximum diversified demand in the order of 1.3 to 2.3 kw which is of relatively minor significance when compared with the heating demand of 7.5 to 8.5 for the heating system. This condition, together with the relative flatness of the daily load curve for the regular residential use, precludes, in any practical way, the introduction of load control or load interlock features to electric space heating, unless the heating itself should be reduced. The possibility of employing off-peak storage to reduce the coincident demand is covered in Chapter 2.

COMMERCIAL ELECTRIC SPACE HEATING LOAD CHARACTERISTICS (*Heat Pumps*)

The economic evaluation of the commercial load is different from the residential. The electric rate for commercial structures is most often a demand type, while that for residential structures is usually on a unit cost basis. Also, the maximum heating and cooling demand in relation to the other load is quite different in the two types of application. In the residence the heating is five to seven times the other load, while in commercial installations it is only two to three times or less. Therefore, the other loads are important contributing factors to the diversified demands and load factors. In fact, the internal heat gains of a commercial building may represent a considerable portion of the heating requirement of the structure and materially change the shape of the load curve. In many modern structures, as shown in Figure 4-3 of Chapter 4, the internal gain can furnish a considerable portion of the heating requirements during the heating season and at some outdoor temperatures, such as 45 F and above (during occupied periods), all of the heating requirements can be supplied from this source.

Because of the usable internal heat gain of a commercial building, the heat pump for heating and cooling, when properly designed and operated, can be made to improve the coincident demand at the time of system peak with a corresponding improvement in the annual load factor. The demand and the annual kilowatthour consumption for commercial heating and cooling systems are therefore not the dominant factors in the design and selection of the electric transmission and distribution system as they are in the evaluations of all-electric residences.

Terminology

Coincidence factor (reciprocal of diversity factor). The ratio of the maximum demand of a group or system as a whole to the sum of the maximum demands of each separate component of the group.

Cost of service. Average cost of all elements of operating expense, taxes, depreciation allowances, plus an adequate return on the investment.

Degree days (base 65). Determined by a summation of the temperature difference between the mean daily temperature and an indoor base temperature arbitrarily selected as 65 F. If no factors were involved, other than indoor-outdoor temperature difference, the base would be 70 F, provided the indoor temperature is maintained at 70 F.

Diversified demand. The coincident maximum demand of a group of customers taken as a whole. Group maximum demands are determined by direct measurement or by the addition of the load curves of the individual customer comprising the group.

Diversity factor. The ratio of the sum of the maximum demand of each separate component of a group to the maximum demand of the group.

Energy use. The kilowatthours supplied to or used by an individual customer or a group of customers.

Load curve. As applied to a customer or group of customers it is a curve of integrated kilowatts of demand vs. time showing the value of the specific integrated demand for each unit of time in the period covered.

Load factor. Ratio of the average demand over a designated period of time to the maximum demand occurring in that period. Load factor, in percentage, may be derived by multiplying the kilowatt-hours in the period by 100 and then dividing by the maximum demand times the number of hours in the period.

Maximum demand. The maximum demand is the greatest of all of the integrated demands of the load under consideration which has occurred during a specified period of time. The maximum demand is determined by means of an integrating demand meter which measures the average demand over a definitely prescribed time interval of 15 min, 30 min, or other such periods.

System maximum demand. The maximum demand of the whole electric supply system. It is coincident maximum demand of the combined classes of customers and includes losses between the customers and the point of measurement of the system maximum demand.

REFERENCES

Achenback, Paul, J. C. Davis, and Wm. T. Smith, *Analysis of Electric Energy Usage in Air Force Houses Equipped with Air-to-Air Heat Pumps,* NBS Monograph 51, U. S. Department of Commerce, National Bureau of Standards, July 13, 1962.

Electrical World, November 1950.

Jordan, R. C., G. A. Erickson, and R. R. Leonard, Energy Sources and Requirements for Residential Heating, *ASHRAE Journal,* 4, No. 1, 33–45 (January 1961).

Sporn, Philip and E. R. Ambrose, Load Characteristics of Five All-Electric Residences Using the Heat Pump for Year-Round Air Conditioning, Paper 52–339, *American Institute of Electrical Engineers Transactions,* 1952.

Chapter 9

Energy Consumption Computations:
Heating and Cooling

It is apparent from a review of the previous chapters that all the factors affecting the performance of electric year-round air conditioning systems must be carefully evaluated in order to determine accurately the annual owning and operating cost. The climatic conditions, the heat loss and heat gain, the type and size of structure, the design of the heating and cooling system, the amount of usable internal heat gain, the ventilation or infiltration air requirement, and the heat source-sink (in the case of the heat pump) are all influencing factors which must be considered in any owning and operating cost computation.

STRUCTURE HEAT LOSS AND HEAT GAIN

The importance of an accurate structure heat loss and heat gain calculation, both for use in designing the system as well as for estimating the annual operating cost, was discussed in Chapter 4. The gross heat loss consists of the conduction loss through the exterior surfaces of the structure and the ventilation or infiltration loss. The heat gain includes the structure's conduction and solar loads, the internal heat gain, and the ventilation or infiltration air quantities.

One important factor which influences the heat gain and heat loss is the wind velocity. Most thermal conduction coefficients and infiltration rates for exterior walls, roofs, and windows are based on a 15 mph wind for the exterior surfaces and on still air for the interior surfaces. It may be justifiable to use such thermal coefficients and infiltration rates to size the equipment for design conditions. In annual operating cost computation, however, it would be more realistic to base particularly the infiltration rates on the average seasonal wind velocity. Unfortunately, it is difficult if not impossible to determine accurately the infiltration rate for a residence, as an example, at either the design or the average operating conditions because of the variables in building construction. There are variations in the width and length of crack around windows or other openings through which air leakage takes place, in wind velocity and direction, and in exposure (with respect to wind direction and adjoining buildings).

The tightness of a window has considerable influence on the infiltration rate as shown in Figure 9-1. An average nonweather-stripped window, with a 10 mph wind, for instance, has a leakage of 21 cfm per hour per foot of crack, and a weatherstripped window has 13 cfm. In a 25 mph wind, these quantities increase to 80 cfm and 49 cfm, respectively. It is important to note that the infiltration rate for a poorly fitted, nonweather-stripped window is about 2½ times greater than the figure given for an average weather-stripped window. Storm sash can reduce leakage as much as 50 percent, and

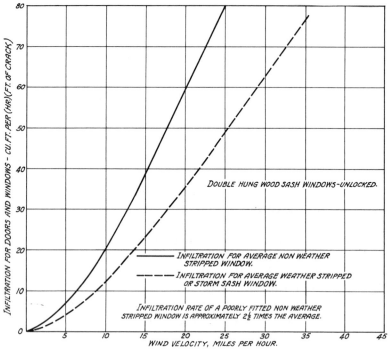

Figure 9-1 The infiltration rate is proportional to the wind velocity. The tightness of the doors or windows has considerable influence on the infiltration rate. After *ASHRAE Guide and Data Book* (1963), Fund. and Equip., Chap. 24, Table 2.

fixed double-sealed windows may reduce the infiltration to practically zero. It is essential, therefore, to have tight-fitting, properly weather-stripped windows and doors to obtain dependable and satisfactory infiltration values and, at the same time, reduce the heat loss to a practical limit. A thorough discussion on storm sash and other recommended heat conservation practices is given in Chapter 6.

CLIMATOLOGICAL DATA

The size of the heating and cooling load and to a large extent the practicability of a given installation are determined by the existing climatic conditions.

Climatological data for most sections of the country are published by the U.S. Department of Commerce Weather Bureau. The product and application manuals of a number of air conditioning manufacturers also include usable weather data for many areas. Probably the most widely used weather data are the daily minimum-maximum temperatures published regularly by the U.S. Government. Although the weather bureau has found that the average of the daily maximum and minimum dry bulb temperatures, at any one station, comes within less than one degree of the hourly daily average, it may be necessary in designing a heat pump system to know the probable daily hourly variation between the recorded maximum and minimum temperatures, as illustrated in Figure 9-2. These data are particularly useful if an off-peak storage system is being contemplated (Chapter 2), or if it is important to evaluate the kilowatt demand at the time of electric utility system peak as discussed in Chapter 8.

The U.S. Weather Bureau also has available for many cities the average degree hour data for a typical 5-year period. Convenient forms for such data are given in Tables 9-1, 9-2, 9-3, and 9-4 and Figures 9-3 through 9-10. Table 9-1 gives the outdoor temperatures and hours of occurrence which can be expected during a 10-month heating season, September through June, in an area with about 4500 degree days, such as Roanoke, Virginia. Columns 2 and 3 under each month give the day and night hours at and below the temperatures shown in column 1 for an average year. Similarly, columns 4 and 5 give the corresponding day and night weighted average temperatures. Table 9-2 gives the same type of data for a 10-month cooling season. For the cooling season, the temperatures in column 1 start at 50 F and increase to 100 F and above. The numbers in columns 2 and 3, under each month, are the day and night hours

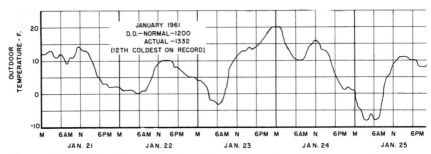

Figure 9-2 The hourly variation in outdoor temperature for 10 consecutive days, during January 1961, for Ft. Wayne, Ind.

TABLE 9-1   Climatological Data for an Area with 4500 Degree Days. Outdoor Temperatures Are Related to Hours of Occurrence and to Weighted Average Temperature for Different Months of Heating Season. (After U.S. Dept. of Commerce Weather Bureau, Asheville, N.C.)

September to January

Outdoor Temp. °F	SEPTEMBER No. of Hrs. Day	Night	Weighted Avg. Temp. Day	Night	OCTOBER No. of Hrs. Day	Night	Weighted Avg. Temp. Day	Night	NOVEMBER No. of Hrs. Day	Night	Weighted Avg. Temp. Day	Night	DECEMBER No. of Hrs. Day	Night	Weighted Avg. Temp. Day	Night	JANUARY No. of Hrs. Day	Night	Weighted Avg. Temp. Day	Night
1	2	3	4	5	2	3	4	5	2	3	4	5	2	3	4	5	2	3	4	5
75	238	320	64	64	333	387	57	54	359	360	47	43	375	372	39	37	372	371	40	39
70	183	266	62	62	302	354	55	54	350	360	46	43	375	372	39	37	369	371	40	39
65	126	181	59	59	252	323	53	52	332	356	45	43	372	372	39	37	365	369	40	39
60	68	93	55	55	198	271	50	50	306	336	44	42	364	371	39	37	354	362	39	38
55	32	45	51	52	142	203	47	48	262	313	41	41	349	360	38	36	335	347	38	37
50	13	13	47	48	92	122	44	44	220	269	39	39	325	342	37	35	304	327	37	36
45	2	2	44	44	51	61	40	40	171	210	36	36	281	311	35	34	258	285	35	35
40	1		40		25	30	36	36	116	134	33	33	206	260	32	33	204	228	32	32
35					9	12	31	33	74	80	30	29	139	174	29	30	131	150	29	30
30					4	2	28	29	31	41	25	25	66	80	26	26	60	67	25	25
25					0				12	21	21	21	23	31	21	22	30	29	21	20
20									5	8	17	18	9	6	18	18	15	14	18	17
15									2	1	14	14	2	2	13	15	4	4	14	13
10																	0			

February to June

FEBRUARY No. of Hrs. Day	Night	Weighted Avg. Temp. Day	Night	MARCH No. of Hrs. Day	Night	Weighted Avg. Temp. Day	Night	APRIL No. of Hrs. Day	Night	Weighted Avg. Temp. Day	Night	MAY No. of Hrs. Day	Night	Weighted Avg. Temp. Day	Night	JUNE No. of Hrs. Day	Night	Weighted Avg. Temp. Day	Night
2	3	4	5	2	3	4	5	2	3	4	5	2	3	4	5	2	3	4	5
336	336	41	40	361	369	47	47	328	350	53	52	266	329	62	61	177	278	68	67
333	335	41	40	349	364	46	46	308	339	52	51	211	282	60	60	111	204	65	65
327	333	40	40	337	351	46	45	282	314	50	50	157	217	57	57	53	93	61	61
313	323	39	39	313	329	44	44	235	269	48	47	104	139	53	54	20	31	56	57
292	304	38	38	269	291	42	42	192	226	46	45	57	79	50	50	7	10	53	52
267	286	37	37	221	243	40	40	136	166	43	43	27	35	46	47	1	1	47	48
241	255	36	35	172	173	37	37	89	115	40	40	11	10	43	43				
180	190	33	33	113	113	34	34	37	54	36	37	2	1	38	39				
113	116	30	29	62	60	31	31	16	16	33	33	1		35					
56	60	26	26	22	23	27	27	3	3	29	29								
21	23	23	22	6	5	23	23												
4	6	19	18	1	1	19	19												
0																			

NOTE: DAY PERIOD IS FROM 6 A.M. TO 6 P.M. – NIGHT PERIOD IS FROM 6 P.M. TO 6 A.M. – TOTAL IS FOR 24 HOUR PERIOD

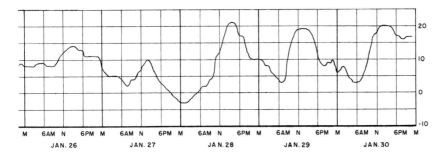

TABLE 9-2   Climatological Data for an Area with 4500 Degree Days. Outdoor Temperatures Are Related to Hours of Occurrence and to Weighted Average Temperature for Different Months of Cooling Season. (After U.S. Dept. of Commerce Weather Bureau, Asheville, N.C.)

March to July

Outdoor Temp. °F	March — No. of Hrs. Day	No. of Hrs. Night	Weighted Avg. Temp. Day	Weighted Avg. Temp. Night	April — Day	Night	Day	Night	May — Day	Night	Day	Night	June — Day	Night	Day	Night	July — Day	Night	Day	Night
1	2	3	4	5	2	3	4	5	2	3	4	5	2	3	4	5	2	3	4	5
100													1		100		2		101	
95													2		98		9	2	98	96
90					0				2	1	91	90	18	4	92	91	30	7	93	92
85					4	1	86	86	32	6	87	87	60	17	88	87	89	23	89	88
80	4	0	81		14	3	83	83	71	23	84	83	127	44	85	84	160	61	86	84
75	13	3	78	78	36	13	79	78	119	50	81	80	198	90	82	80	226	123	83	80
70	25	11	75	73	58	25	77	75	173	102	78	76	265	180	79	76	297	244	81	76
65	39	24	72	69	86	55	73	70	226	174	76	72	316	289	77	73	344	335	79	74
60	65	49	68	66	137	101	69	66	280	249	73	69	344	337	76	71	368	365	78	73
55	111	93	63	62	178	146	66	63	322	303	71	67	355	351	76	71	371	370	77	73
50	163	140	60	58	237	205	63	60	350	343	69	65	359	359	75	70	371	370	77	73

August to December

August — No. of Hrs. Day	No. of Hrs. Night	Weighted Avg. Temp. Day	Weighted Avg. Temp. Night	September — Day	Night	Day	Night	October — Day	Night	Day	Night	November — Day	Night	Day	Night	December — Day	Night	Day	Night
2	3	4	5	2	3	4	5	2	3	4	5	2	3	4	5	2	3	4	5
1		95		1		96													
23	4	91	90	10	1	92	91	0											
84	22	88	87	41	7	88	87	6		87									
162	52	85	84	84	19	85	84	21	2	83	82								
226	111	83	80	132	48	82	79	44	7	80	78	2		76					
296	236	80	76	190	114	79	75	83	23	76	74	14	1	72	70				
348	337	78	73	245	195	76	72	131	60	73	69	33	6	69	67				
369	369	77	72	303	284	73	69	188	115	69	66	62	30	66	63	13	1	63	61
372	372	77	72	330	325	72	67	243	186	67	62	105	54	62	60	29	17	60	57
372	372	77	72	347	351	71	66	289	261	64	59	149	101	59	56	58	36	56	54

NOTE: DAY PERIOD IS FROM 6 A.M. TO 6 P.M. — NIGHT PERIOD IS FROM 6 P.M. TO 6 A.M. — TOTAL IS FOR 24 HOUR PERIOD

TABLE 9-3   Climatological Data for an Area with 6300 Degree Days.
Outdoor Temperatures Are Related to Hours of Occurrence and to
Weighted Average Temperature for Different Months of Heating Season.
(After U.S. Dept. of Commerce Weather Bureau, Asheville, N.C.)

September to January

Outdoor Temp °F	September No. of Hrs. Day	Night	September Weighted Avg. Temp. Day	Night	October No. of Hrs. Day	Night	October Weighted Avg. Temp. Day	Night	November No. of Hrs. Day	Night	November Weighted Avg. Temp. Day	Night	December No. of Hrs. Day	Night	December Weighted Avg. Temp. Day	Night	January No. of Hrs. Day	Night	January Weighted Avg. Temp. Day	Night
1	2	3	4	5	2	3	4	5	2	3	4	5	2	3	4	5	2	3	4	5
75	273	349	62	57	354	372	53	46	357	358	39	36	371	372	28	25	372	372	25	23
70	225	316	60	56	336	370	52	46	354	358	38	36	371	372	28	25	372	372	25	23
65	163	260	56	53	302	357	50	46	347	357	38	36	371	372	28	25	372	372	25	23
60	112	213	53	51	261	332	47	44	335	347	37	34	371	372	28	25	372	372	25	23
55	63	149	50	48	204	296	45	43	320	334	36	33	369	371	28	25	372	371	25	23
50	28	97	45	45	151	243	42	40	296	323	35	33	365	370	28	25	367	368	25	23
45	11	41	41	41	98	180	39	38	259	297	33	31	352	363	27	25	360	365	25	23
40	4	16	36	37	43	108	34	34	220	251	31	30	335	351	26	24	345	350	24	22
35	2	4	34	34	21	57	30	31	155	196	28	27	303	322	25	23	313	323	22	21
30					10	24	27	27	96	125	25	23	209	244	21	20	261	261	20	18
25					3	5	22	22	47	81	21	20	127	164	16	16	170	208	16	15
20					1	1	19	18	16	38	17	17	80	112	12	11	108	137	12	11
15									4	10	14	14	52	64	9	8	63	90	7	7
10									0	0			26	35	6	4	34	50	3	3

February to June

February No. of Hrs. Day	Night	February Weighted Avg. Temp. Day	Night	March No. of Hrs. Day	Night	March Weighted Avg. Temp. Day	Night	April No. of Hrs. Day	Night	April Weighted Avg. Temp. Day	Night	May No. of Hrs. Day	Night	May Weighted Avg. Temp. Day	Night	June No. of Hrs. Day	Night	June Weighted Avg. Temp. Day	Night
2	3	4	5	2	3	4	5	2	3	4	5	2	3	4	5	2	3	4	5
338	338	26	24	369	372	41	37	352	360	50	41	310	369	60	54	244	342	67	61
338	338	26	24	365	372	39	36	339	358	46	41	275	353	58	53	160	309	63	60
338	338	26	24	362	370	39	36	319	354	45	41	213	318	55	51	94	235	60	57
338	338	26	24	343	364	37	34	293	339	43	40	153	262	52	49	46	153	56	54
334	338	26	24	321	349	36	33	258	315	41	38	98	201	48	46	18	85	52	50
328	335	25	23	293	332	34	32	221	288	39	37	57	146	44	43	4	41	49	47
317	325	25	23	263	312	33	31	180	244	37	35	32	93	42	40		10		43
299	314	24	22	217	278	31	29	119	186	34	33	10	46	38	37		1		39
276	290	23	21	163	223	28	27	63	118	30	29	2	15	34	33				
216	237	20	18	90	149	24	24	28	64	27	26		2		29				
145	168	16	14	46	78	21	20	8	22	23	23								
94	119	12	10	18	29	17	15	1	2	19	19								
56	83	7	7	6	13	12	12												
33	53	3	3	1	4	5	7												

NOTE: DAY PERIOD IS FROM 6 A.M. TO 6 P.M. — NIGHT PERIOD IS FROM 6 P.M. TO 6 A.M. — TOTAL IS FOR 24 HOUR PERIOD

during which the temperature in column 1 will be equalled or
exceeded. In the same manner, columns 4 and 5 give the corresponding weighted average temperature. Similarly, Tables 9-3 and 9-4 give
typical temperature data for an area with about 6300 degree days,
such as Fort Wayne, Indiana.

From data similar to those given in Tables 9-1 through 9-4 temperature curves can be prepared for any given area, as shown in
Figures 9-3 through 9-10. Figures 9-3, 9-4, 9-5, and 9-6 give the frequency and weighted average temperatures during the heating and
cooling cycle for an area averaging 4000 to 5000 degree days. Figures
9-7 through 9-10 give similar temperature data for areas with about

TABLE 9-4 Climatological Data for an Area with 6300 Degree Days. Outdoor Temperatures Are Related to Hours of Occurrence and to Weighted Average Temperature for Different Months of Cooling Season. (After U.S. Dept. of Commerce Weather Bureau, Asheville, N.C.)

March to July

OUTDOOR TEMP °F	MARCH No. of Hrs. Day	Night	MARCH Weighted Avg. Temp. Day	Night	APRIL No. of Hrs. Day	Night	APRIL Weighted Avg. Temp. Day	Night	MAY No. of Hrs. Day	Night	MAY Weighted Avg. Temp. Day	Night	JUNE No. of Hrs. Day	Night	JUNE Weighted Avg. Temp. Day	Night	JULY No. of Hrs. Day	Night	JULY Weighted Avg. Temp. Day	Night
1	2	3	4	5	2	3	4	5	2	3	4	5	2	3	4	5	2	3	4	5
105																	2		106	
100																	9	1	103	101
95																	16	3	100	98
90													4		91		39	5	95	95
85									8		86		20	1	87	87	98	13	90	90
80	1		80		1		80		35	2	82	82	67	9	83	82	181	35	86	85
75	3		78		9	0	77		63	10	80	78	132	22	80	79	250	78	84	80
70	7		74		24	2	74	73	108	24	76	74	215	65	77	74	307	172	82	76
65	12	2	72	67	45	8	71	68	169	64	73	70	278	146	75	70	345	259	80	73
60	33	10	65	62	73	26	67	63	235	121	70	66	314	222	75	67	364	321	79	71
55	55	26	62	59	109	51	64	60	284	181	68	63	350	272	73	65	371	355	79	69
50	84	44	58	56	145	79	61	57	325	235	66	61	362	317	72	64	372	368	79	69

August to December

AUGUST No. of Hrs. Day	Night	AUGUST Weighted Avg. Temp. Day	Night	SEPTEMBER No. of Hrs. Day	Night	SEPTEMBER Weighted Avg. Temp. Day	Night	OCTOBER No. of Hrs. Day	Night	OCTOBER Weighted Avg. Temp. Day	Night	NOVEMBER No. of Hrs. Day	Night	NOVEMBER Weighted Avg. Temp. Day	Night	DECEMBER No. of Hrs. Day	Night	DECEMBER Weighted Avg. Temp. Day	Night
2	3	4	5	2	3	4	5	2	3	4	5	2	3	4	5	2	3	4	5
0																			
6		97																	
25	2	93	92	1		91													
82	7	89	87	17		87		0											
162	26	85	83	52	2	83	82	10		82									
237	71	83	79	97	15	80	77	21		79		0							
292	153	81	75	148	55	77	73	42	4	75	71	5		72					
336	248	79	72	209	108	74	70	81	17	71	68	12	2	69	66				
359	311	78	70	257	159	72	68	120	47	68	64	25	14	65	62				
367	350	77	69	304	221	70	65	178	83	64	61	42	25	62	60	2	1	57	57
371	365	77	68	337	276	68	62	233	142	61	57	68	41	58	57	8	2	53	54

NOTE: Day Period is from 6 A.M. to 6 P.M. – Night Period is from 6 P.M. to 6 A.M. – Total is for 24 Hour Period

5500 to 6500 degree days. These temperature curves may be more convenient than the tabulations and give a better understanding of the temperature range and variation for the particular area. It is noted that the curves for the two areas are similar in general contour but vary in the slope of the center portion and in the end points.

Temperature data in the form shown by the tables and figures will also provide degree day information if it is not readily available for a particular location. Degree days are generally computed from the summation of the daily difference between a predetermined base temperature (such as 65 F) and the daily mean of the maximum-minimum temperature. As a substitute the hours and the weighted

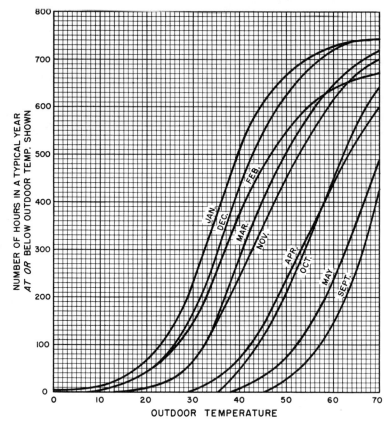

Figure 9-3 Climatological data for an area with 4000 to 5000 degree days. The outdoor temperatures are related to the hours of occurrence of the different months of the heating season. After U.S. Dept. of Commerce Weather Bureau, Asheville, N.C.

average temperature (below 65 F, for example) for a particular month can be obtained from climatological data such as Tables 9-1 and 9-3 or from curves such as those in Figures 9-3 and 9-5 or 9-7 and 9-9. For example, during the month of January the hours below 65 F are 734, and the corresponding weighted average temperature is 39.5 F for the geographic area represented by Table 9-4. The degree days for the month therefore, equal (65 F − 39.5 F)(734/24) or 780.

OUTDOOR DESIGN TEMPERATURE SELECTION

The sizing of the equipment and to a lesser extent the annual operating cost are related to outdoor design temperature. With climatological data, such as those in Tables 9-1 and 9-2, it is possible to choose a design temperature for both the heating and the cooling cycles which will result in the most satisfactory and most economical system.

Some design engineers may select an extremely low temperature or may purposely oversize the equipment in order to be safe under all operating conditions. The main adverse effect of following this procedure, other than the increase in first cost, is the possible increase in the kilowatt demand and the resultingly higher electric rate as explained in Chapter 8. It is not good practice to use a maximum or a minimum temperature as a basis for the design of a heating and cooling system. Nor can the best equipment selection be obtained by adding a number of degrees to the minimum temperature to

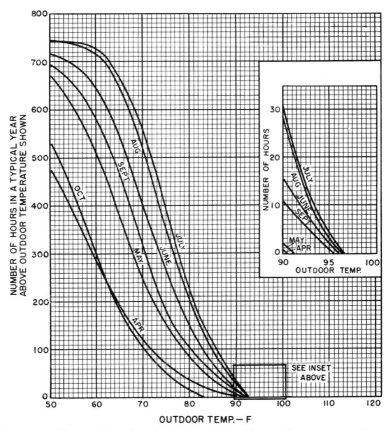

Figure 9-4 Climatological data for an area with 4000 to 5000 degree days. The outdoor temperatures are related to the hours of occurrence for the different months of the cooling season. After U.S. Dept. of Commerce Weather Bureau, Asheville, N.C.

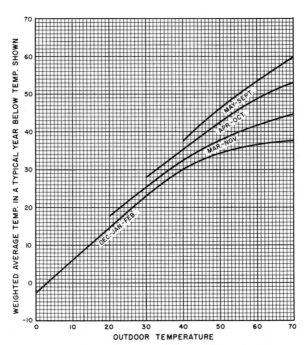

Figure 9-5 Climatological data for an area with 4000 to 5000 degree days. The outdoor temperatures are related to the weighted average temperatures for the different months of the heating season. After U.S. Dept. of Commerce Weather Bureau, Asheville, N.C.

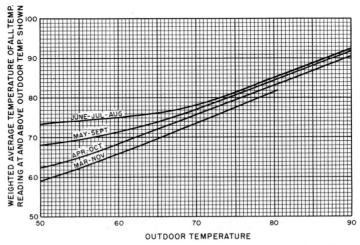

Figure 9-6 Climatological data for area with 4000 to 5000 degree days. The outdoor temperatures are related to the weighted average temperature for the different months of the cooling season. After U.S. Dept. of Commerce Weather Bureau, Asheville, N.C.

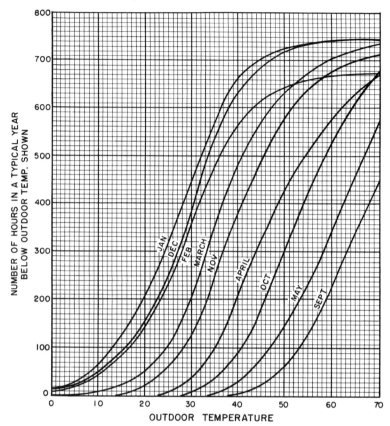

Figure 9-7 Climatological data for an area with 5500 to 6500 degree days. The outdoor temperatures are related to the hours of occurrence for the different months of the heating season. After U.S. Dept. of Commerce Weather Bureau, Asheville, N.C.

obtain a heating design or by subtracting a number of degrees from the maximum temperature to obtain the cooling design.

The preferable procedure is to analyze the weather records in order to determine the probability of occurrence of certain low temperatures. The *ASHRAE Guide* lists for principal United States cities the frequency of occurrence of winter temperatures within the periods of 40, 20, 13, 10, and 5 years. For the usual structure, under typical conditions, it is generally recommended that the minimum outdoor temperature with a frequency of once in 13 years be selected for equipment design. In selecting the design temperature for the cooling cycle, the wet bulb as well as the dry bulb temperatures must be taken into consideration. The ASHRAE Guide also lists the fre-

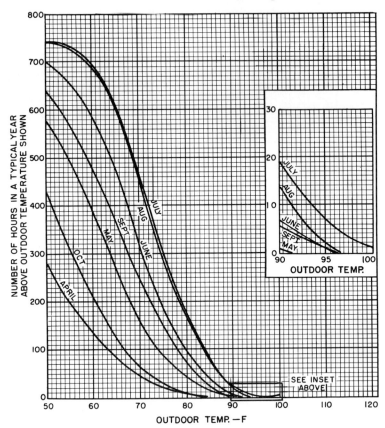

Figure 9-8 Climatological data for an area with 5500 to 6500 degree days. The outdoor temperatures are related to the hours of occurrence for the different months of the cooling season. After U.S. Dept. of Commerce Weather Bureau, Asheville, N.C.

quency of occurrence of summer dry bulb and wet bulb temperatures for a number of cities. As a general rule, the maximum dry bulb and wet bulb temperatures do not occur simultaneously during the cooling season. A wide variation in one temperature may be accompanied by a relatively small change in the other. This fact must be taken into consideration in the selection of dry bulb and wet bulb temperatures. Some precaution must be exercised in using weather data based on airport readings. The urban area of a large city usually shows a warmer atmosphere than suburban or outlying regions. The design temperatures or degree days, particularly for larger cities, must accordingly be adjusted if airport data is used as a base.

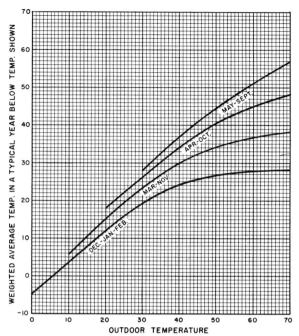

Figure 9-9 Climatological data for an area with 5500 to 6500 degree days. The outdoor temperatures are related to the weighted average temperature for the different months of the heating season. After U.S. Dept. of Commerce Weather Bureau, Asheville, N.C.

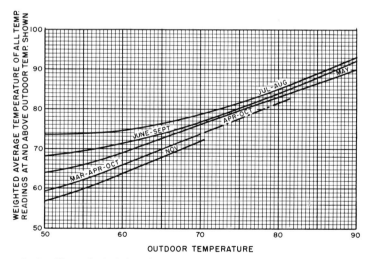

Figure 9-10 Climatological data for an area with 5500 to 6500 degree days. The outdoor temperatures are related to the weighted average temperature for the different months of the cooling season. After U.S. Dept. of Commerce Weather Bureau, Asheville, N.C.

163

The thermal "flywheel" action of a structure is an important consideration in determining both the heat gain and heat loss. This, however, is dependent both on the type of structure involved and on the duration of the extreme temperatures. The load on the equipment is not generally affected by a temperature fluctuation of short duration. On the other hand, the load on the equipment may be proportionally affected if a minimum temperature during the heating cycle or a maximum temperature during the cooling cycle is experienced for a period of several days. This is particularly true if more than the usual amount of outside air is taken into the conditioned space during these periods.

HEATING OPERATING HOURS

The temperature curves given in Figures 9-3 and 9-7 show that the percentage of the heating hours at the selected outdoor design temperature are relatively small and represent a rather insignificant portion of the total energy requirement. This fact is perhaps better illustrated by Figure 9-11 which gives the operating hours of the heating equipment at 25, 50, 75, and 100 percent capacity for four

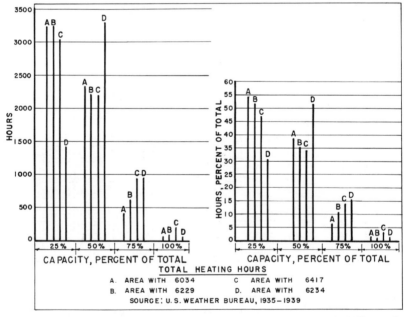

Figure 9-11 Operating hours of heating equipment at 25, 50, 75, and 100% capacity for a structure in several geographic areas.

different geographic areas. It can be noted that the need for 100 percent heating capacity in the four areas ranges from 0.9 to 3.2 percent of the total heating hours; 75 percent of heating capacity ranges from 6.7 to 15.2 percent of the total heating hours; 50 percent heating capacity ranges from 34.7 to 52.7 percent of the total heating hours, and 25 percent heating capacity ranges from 30.8 to 54.0 percent of the total heating hours. Therefore, the outdoor temperatures are such, in these four areas, that 50 percent or less of the heating capacity is needed 82.1 to 92.4 percent of the total heating hours.

When the larger percentage of the heating operating hours occurs at the higher outdoor temperatures the air source heat pump will be able to operate at reduced loads, lower head pressures, higher suction pressures, and with little or no supplemental heat. This favorable operating condition results in a relatively high average performance factor which will make the heat pump attractive and competitive in many areas.

COOLING OPERATING HOURS

Normally the percentage of operating hours at full cooling capacity will be relatively small, as indicated in Figures 9-4, 9-8 and Figure 9-12. The latter figure gives the estimated operating hours of the cooling equipment at 25, 50, 75, and 100 percent capacities for the same four geographic areas used for the heating cycle evaluation. The need for 100 percent cooling capacity averages about 12 percent of the total hours for 75 percent capacity averages 31 percent, for 50 percent about 45 percent, and for 25 percent averages 12 percent. The outdoor temperatures in these four areas, therefore, are such that 50 percent or less of the cooling capacity is required about 57 percent of the cooling season.

It is generally agreed by most air conditioning engineers and has been substantiated in several instances by test data that the mechanical cooling equipment for commercial buildings must be operated when the outdoor temperature is 55 F and above during occupied periods and 75 F and above during the unoccupied periods. Some judgment must be exercized in using test data and design factors, however, since the amount of internal heat gain and size of equipment selected, in relation to the total calculated load will influence the partial load operating hours.

It can be noted from Figure 9-12 that the cooling hours for the four areas under consideration will range from 2050 to 2600. The refrigeration equipment, however, will operate partially loaded during about 87 percent of this time. Some engineers convert these

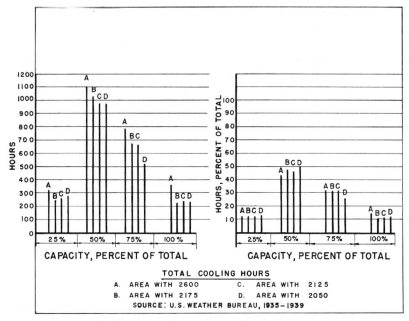

Figure 9-12   Operating hours of cooling equipment at 25, 50, 75, and 100% capacity for a structure in several geographic areas.

operating hours at partial loads to equivalent full load operating hours. The resulting equivalent full load hours are then multiplied by the full load power input (of the refrigeration equipment and all auxiliaries) to obtain the seasonal kilowatthours. This procedure is based on the erroneous assumption that the refrigeration equipment operates at the same efficiency under all loading conditions and that the power input to all of the auxiliaries is proportional to the load. It is for this reason that the use of equivalent full load operating hours is not realistic or accurate for any type of comfort cooling system.

ENERGY CONSUMPTION, RESISTANCE HEATING

The energy consumption for a given heating season can be predicted with a reasonable degree of accuracy by equation 9-1, if it is possible to establish accurate *net* heat loss figures. This particular equation is usually referred to as "the calculated heat loss method,"

$$\text{kwhr} = \frac{H_D(t_i - t_o)N}{3413 \times E} \tag{9-1}$$

where kwhr = quantity of heating energy for period indicated

H = calculated heat loss, Btuh/°F indoor-outdoor design temperature difference (including infiltration or ventilation load)

H_D = net heat loss

t_i = average inside temperature (°F) during heating period

t_o = average outdoor temperature (°F) during heating period

N = hours during heating season; a period from September 1 to June 1 equals 273 days × 24 hours per day or 6552 hours

E = seasonal efficiency = 1.00 for in-the-room resistance heating

DD = degree days with 65 F base

PF = seasonal heat pump performance factor

Unfortunately, for the reasons previously stated, accurate average seasonal net heat loss figures cannot be predicted. Therefore the results from equation 9-1 seldom agree with the actual consumption. When the gross calculated heat loss at design condition is used in the equation, the results are always on the high side and give inaccurately high operating cost estimates.

For several decades the "degree day method" given by equation 9-2 has been used for computing the annual fuel consumption of buildings.

$$\text{kwhr} = \frac{H(\text{DD})24}{3413 \times E} \tag{9-2}$$

Practical experience has shown that this method gives abnormally high values when used for estimating energy requirements of fully insulated buildings utilizing electric heating. This is attributable to the lower air infiltration rate (due to the absence of combustion air requirements), to the higher overall seasonal operating efficiencies of electric equipment, and to the insufficient credit for the electric power consumed by the lights, appliances, hot water heaters, and other internal gains. The electric power when converted to heat will, in part, supplement the output of the heating system and thus reduce the heating kilowatthours. The "degree day method" is based on the field tests of the late 1930's and does not include sufficient credit for internal gains. The average electric power consumption in the home for the past ten years (for all customers), for example, has increased from about 2000 kwhrs per year to close to 5000 kwhrs per year. For an all-electric customer, this annual consumption (excluding heating) averages about 7500 to 8000 kwhrs annually, which further increases the inaccuracy of the estimated annual energy consumption for heating when equation 9-2 is used.

A number of heat factors have been developed to make the degree day formula applicable to electric heating systems. Many electric utilities throughout the country have made numerous field tests to study load characteristics of resistance space heating and to determine a dependable usage factor which will bring the estimated annual energy consumption in agreement with the actual. Based on these studies the formula recommended by the electrical industry is

$$\text{kwhr} = \frac{H(\text{DD})C}{3413 \times E} \tag{9-3}$$

where C is usage factor based on actual installation experience in the particular area

and H is the calculated heat loss based on an air infiltration rate of ¾ air changes per hour.

The usage factor C has been found to vary generally between 16 and 20 depending upon the geographic location, the internal heat gain,

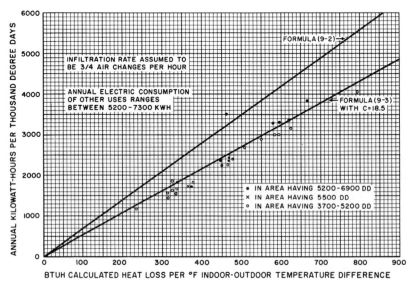

Figure 9-13 Annual kilowatthours per thousand degree days for individual residences located in different areas, compared with corresponding heat loss.

and the design and operating cycle of the system. Generally a C value of about 18.5 has been found to be applicable in areas with 3500 to 6500 degree days.

Some idea of how the actual measured heating kilowatthours compare with the estimated energy consumption equation is given in Figure 9-13. For such an evaluation the heat loss of the houses must all be figured on the same basis of infiltration rate and other influencing factors. Due to the different living habits and the amount of useful internal gain in the individual houses, a variation of plus or minus 10 percent can still be expected between the predicted and the actual. The variation in degree days from year to year is also a factor. It must be remembered that the degree days published by the U.S. Weather Bureau for different geographic areas represent long term averages and cannot be expected to coincide with any single year. Individual yearly degree days may vary as much as plus or minus 20 percent from the long term averages with proportional variations in the heating energy consumption.

ENERGY CONSUMPTION, HEAT PUMP (*Using Air as Heat Source-Heat Sink*)

It is important to follow an accurate and dependable method of determining the heating and cooling energy consumption regardless of the type of equipment being used. This is particularly true if a comparison is to be made of several different systems. A heat pump evaluation using air as the heat source and sink requires a little more care than most systems, because of the heating output and the corresponding performance factor decrease with a drop in outdoor temperature, and the supplemental resistance heat is used generally at the lower outdoor temperatures.

The basic annual energy consumption equation for air source heat pumps is given by equation 9-4,

$$\text{kwhr} = \frac{H_D(\text{DD})(24)}{3413 \times \text{PF}}. \tag{9-4}$$

This basic equation is very similar to the resistance heating equation 9-2 except that the performance factor (PF) has been substituted for the efficiency (E). The performance factor is the average seasonal coefficient of performance. The C factors previously mentioned in connection with residential resistance heating computation are not applicable to commercial installations because of the wide variation in the useful heat component; consequently a method for using the net heat loss H_D must be developed.

The annual energy consumption for a water heat source-sink heat pump can be found with equation 9-4 by inserting the applicable performance factor and the proper H_D value. The performance factor for the water heat source-sink heat pump during the heating cycle particularly is reasonably constant and independent of the outdoor temperatures. This is not the case, however, with the air heat source unit. It is shown in Figure 8-8 of Chapter 8 that the coefficient of performance of an air heat source-sink heat pump is directly related to the outdoor temperature and as a result must be keyed to the expected hours of operation at the various outdoor temperatures to obtain a reliable seasonal performance factor.

The hours of operation and the corresponding weighted average temperature are obtained from climatological data such as illustrated by Table 9-1. These temperature data are required for estimating the monthly kilowatt demand and annual kilowatthour consumption for the heat pump equipment and, in addition, are needed to obtain the monthly and yearly supplemental resistance heating requirements and to determine the amount of useful internal heat gain. One of several procedures for obtaining this required information is first presented as an outline and then is illustrated by means of an example computation.

PROCEDURE FOR ESTIMATING THE ANNUAL ENERGY CONSUMPTION

This procedure has been found useful as a guide to make certain that all of the important items are considered and in turn to be assured that a reasonably accurate annual energy consumption and corresponding operating cost estimate is obtained.

1. Plot the structure heat loss and heat gain and the equipment heating and cooling capacities as shown in Figure 9-14. The equipment heating and cooling capacities at the various operating conditions are obtained from manufacturers' published data.

Heating. This figure shows the structure gross heat loss, heat loss during occupied periods, heat loss during unoccupied periods, and the system heating capacity at various outdoor temperatures. The calculated gross heat loss, less the useful heat gain, equals the heat loss during the occupied period. In addition, the calculated gross heat loss with the reduced ventilation requirements equals the heat loss during the unoccupied period. The changeover temperature during the occupied period and the balance points during both the

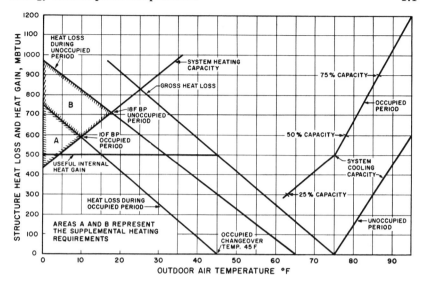

Figure 9-14 Structure heat loss and heat gain at various outdoor temperatures, compared with heat pump having a 100-ton cooling capacity.

occupied and unoccupied periods as well as the supplemental heating requirements can also be obtained from Figure 9-14.

Cooling. This figure shows the structure heat gain during occupied and unoccupied periods and the system cooling capacity (divided into four equal parts) at various outdoor temperatures.

2. Plot in the form of Figure 9-15 the *kilowatt demand* at various outdoor temperatures for compressor, heat source-sink fans, and other heat auxiliaries. These data can be obtained from the manufacturer's data.

3. Compile the weather data in the form shown by Tables 9-1 and 9-2 or Figures 9-3 through 9-6 to show the average temperatures and hours of occurrance for the range of outdoor temperatures experienced during both the heating and cooling cycles for the given area.

4. Record the data and follow the procedure as outlined by Table 9-5 for the heating cycle and Table 9-6 for the cooling cycle for each month of the year.

5. Use the instructions and procedures as outlined in Tables 9-5 and 9-6 to determine the hours, the average outdoor temperature, and corresponding kilowatthours.

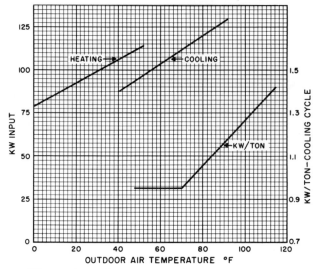

Figure 9-15   Kilowatt demand at various outdoor temperatures for compressor and heat source-sink fans of a heat pump system having a 100-ton cooling capacity.

EXAMPLE OF THE RECOMMENDED PROCEDURE FOR ESTIMATING THE ANNUAL ENERGY CONSUMPTION

An example of using the recommended procedure for estimating the annual energy consumption is given in Table 9-5 for the month of January and in Table 9-6 for the month of July.

The example is based on an installation with a design cooling capacity of 100 tons. It is to be noted that in estimating the heating energy during January, the defrosting kilowatthours were excluded. From Figure 4-11, Chapter 4, it can be concluded that the kilowatthours for defrosting are only approximately 2 or 3 percent of the total consumption for the three coldest months and, therefore, can be neglected without causing an appreciable error in the annual energy consumption.

Table 9-5 shows the estimated heat pump (compressor-outdoor fan combination) heating energy consumption and the supplemental resistance for January to be 19,145 kwhr for area 1 and 47,520 kwhr for area 2. Similarly, Table 9-6 shows the estimated cooling energy consumption for July to be 32,290 kwhr for area 1 and 31,741 kwhr for area 2. Areas 1 and 2 are locations with about 4500 degree days and 6300 degrees respectively. It is interesting to note that the in-

TABLE 9-5 Examples of Recommended Procedure for Estimating Energy Requirements of Heat Pump Compressor—Outdoor Air Heat Source-Sink Fan Combinations

A. Heating for Month of January

		Area 1		Area 2	
		Occupied Period	Unoccupied Period	Occupied Period	Unoccupied Period
1. Design cooling capacity of heat pump system	tons	100	100	100	100
2. Operating temperatures from Figure 9-14					
a. indoor temperature	°F	75	65	75	65
b. changeover temperature	°F	45	65	45	65
c. balance point (B.P.)	°F	10	18	10	18
3. Conditions at the average outdoor temperature, below balance point	°F	—	16	3	10
a. Duration: Table 9-1 or Figs. 9-3 and 9-5	hours	—	9	34	116
b. Structure heat loss: Fig. 9-14	MBtuh	—	730	685	820
c. Heat pump capacity: Fig. 9-14	MBtuh	—	675	475	585
d. Booster heat $\dfrac{(3b-3c)\times 3a}{3413}$	kwhr	—	145	2,100	8,000
4. Conditions at the average outdoor temperature, below changeover temperature	°F	35	39	23	25
a. Duration: Table 9-1 or Figs. 9-3 and 9-5	hours	258	369	360	372
b. Structure heat loss: Fig. 9-14	MBtuh	175	385	360	600
c. Heat pump capacity: Fig. 9-14	MBtuh	980	1,040	790	820
d. Kw demand of compressor and heat source fan: Fig. 9-15	kw	102	105	94	96
e. $kwhr = \dfrac{(4b\times 4a)-(3d\times 3413)}{4c}\times 4d$	kwhr	4,700	14,300	14,520	22,900
5. Kilowatthours for month		4,700	14,445	16,620	30,900
6. Total kwhr for month: occupied and unoccupied hours		19,145		47,520	

TABLE 9-6 Examples of Recommended Procedure for Estimating Energy Requirements of Heat Pump Compressor—Outdoor Air Heat Source-Sink Fan Combinations

B. Cooling for Month of July

		Area 1		Area 2	
		Occupied Period	Unoccupied Period	Occupied Period	Unoccupied Period
1. Design cooling capacity of heat pump system	tons	100	—	100	—
2. Outdoor temperature corresponding to partial loads	°F				
a. 25 percent		55–60	75–85	55–60	75–85
b. 50 percent		60–75	85 and above	60–75	85 and above
c. 75 percent		75–85	—	75–85	—
d. 100 percent		85 and above	—	85 and above	—
3. Hours of occurrence at partial loads: Table 9-2 or Fig. 9-4	hours				
a. 25 percent		3	100	7	65
b. 50 percent		142	23	114	13
c. 75 percent		137	—	152	—
d. 100 percent		89	—	98	—

4. Average outdoor temperature at partial load					
a. 25 percent		57	82	57	80
b. 50 percent		70	89	71	90
c. 75 percent		82	—	82	—
d. 100 percent		89	—	90	—
5. Cooling requirements at partial loads: load (%) × design heat gain (tons) × duration (hours)	ton-hours				
a. 25 percent		25×3=75	25×100=2,500	25×7=175	25×65=1,620
b. 50 percent		50×142=7,100	50×123=1,150	50×114=5,700	50×13=650
c. 75 percent		75×137=10,300	—	75×152=11,400	—
d. 100 percent		100×89=8,900	—	100×98=9,800	—
6. Kilowatthours at partial loads: kw per ton (Fig. 9-15) × ton-hours Item 5)	kwh				
a. 25 percent		0.95×75=70	1.08×2,500=2,700	0.95×175=166	1.05×1,620=1,700
b. 50 percent		.95×7,100=6,740	1.15×1,150=1,480	0.95×5,700=5,420	1.16×650=755
c. 75 percent		1.08×10,300=11,100	—	1.08×11,400=12,300	—
d. 100 percent		1.15×8,900=10,200	—	1.16×9,800=11,400	—
7. Kilowatthours for month		28,110	4,180	29,286	2,455
8. Total kilowatthours for occupied and unoccupied periods		32,290		31,741	

crease in heating kilowatthours between areas 1 and 2 for the coldest month is somewhat proportional to the degree days in the two areas. When the entire heating season is considered it will be found that the kilowatthours will have a much more direct relationship to the respective degree days of the two areas.

It is important to note that heating and cooling kilowatthours, in the example illustrated by Tables 9-5 and 9-6, are based on a 12-hr occupied period and a 12-hr unoccupied period and on maintaining a 75 F indoor temperature every hour of the day and every day of the year. The normal occupancy of most commercial structures and many industrial buildings is limited to an average of about 8 to 10 hours per day for 5 days per week. For most of Saturday and all of Sunday, therefore, the building can be considered unoccupied. Also, it may be that the heating indoor temperature will be reduced 5 to 10 degrees and the cooling indoor temperature raised an equal amount during the unoccupied periods. Consequently, a suitable correction factor must be applied to the hours used in the computation to compensate for the variation in occupancy and in the average indoor temperature.

SUMMARY TABULATION GUIDE FOR OPERATING COST

The electric tariff, for other than residential installations, is usually based on the monthly integrated kilowatt demand for either 15-, 30-, or 60-min intervals. Consequently, it is necessary to know the monthly kilowatt demand and the resulting kilowatthours for the basic electric load, as well as for the heat pump or any other electric equipment, in order to apply the proper electric tariff. It is most convenient to tabulate the monthly load characteristics in a form similar to that given in Table 9-7. The base load, shown in columns 1, 2, and 3, includes lighting, elevators, office machinery, supply and exhaust fans, circulating pumps, and similar items which are normally essential to a structure but are not affected by a particular air conditioning design. For the heat pump (columns 4, 5, and 6) it is preferable to include only the coincident demand and the kilowatthours of the refrigeration compressors, the outdoor fans, and the associated components not included in the base load. The heat pump maximum coincident demand for the month during either the heating or the cooling cycle is the product of the maximum non-coincident of the equipment and the coincident factor. The heat pump coincident demand can then be added directly to the base demand (column 1) in order to obtain the total building demand

TABLE 9-7   Operating Cost Summary of Commercial and Industrial Heat Pump Systems

| Period | Basic—Electric (Lighting and Miscellaneous) | | | Heat Pump | | | Supplemental Resistance Heating (If used) | | Total Heating and Cooling | Total Electric Load (Including Basic) | | |
	Demand kw (1)	kwh (2)	Cost $ (3)	Coincident Demand kw (4)	Heat kwh (5)	Cool kwh (6)	kw (7)	kwh (8)	kwh (9)	kw (10)	kwh (11)	Cost $ (12)
Sept.												
Oct.												
Nov.												
Dec.												
Jan.	240	69,000		65	19,000	—	70	145	19,145	375	88,145	
Feb.												
March												
April												
May												
June												
July	200	62,000		90	—	32,300	—	—	32,300	290	94,300	
Aug.												

(column 10). The coincident factor applied to the heat pump non-coincident demand will depend on the geographic location, type of structure, useful internal gain and on the setting of the controls which operate the system.

After the monthly total demands and corresponding kilowatthours (columns 10 and 11) are computed, it is possible by referring to the proper electric utilities' tariffs to compute the operating cost of the basic electric load (column 3) and of the total building load (column 12). The difference between the two figures represents the operating cost of the electric heating and cooling system.

OPERATING DATA ON ACTUAL INSTALLATION

The many types of structures combined with the variable designs, operating cycles, and application practices make it difficult to find a basis for correlating the operating data of different industrial and commercial heat pump installations. Some relationship seems to exist between the net heat loss per degree F indoor-outdoor temperature difference and the heating kilowatthours per 1000 degree days as illustrated in Figure 9-16. It is to be noted, however, that all of these systems are similar in design, ventilation air usage, and lighting. These and other factors which influence the heat loss have fairly accurately been established by field measurements. Nevertheless, such data, with the proper precautions, are very useful and informative when used in conjunction with the recommended procedures as outlined in Tables 9-5 and 9-6 for estimating the energy consumption of other similar installations.

Other useful data to evaluate the design and operating characteristics of heat pump installation are given by Tables 9-8 and 9-9. This is the design and measured operating data for a four-storied, modern, all-electric department store which is listed as item 8 in Figure 9-16. The average illumination for the structure is 40 to 50 foot-candles supplemented by a number of industrial spot lights. The air conditioning system has a cooling capacity of 313 tons. The annual 554,939 kilowatthours for heating and cooling represent a consumption of about 6.6 kilowatthours per sq ft per year, and is equivalent to approximately 23 percent of the lighting and other miscellaneous electric usage in the building. Such practical and economical heat pump systems, when compared realistically and accurately with other heating and cooling systems have been found to have a decided advantage in annual owning and operating costs. In addition, the heat pump has many desirable inherent characteristics which makes it a very satisfactory and acceptable year-round air conditioning system.

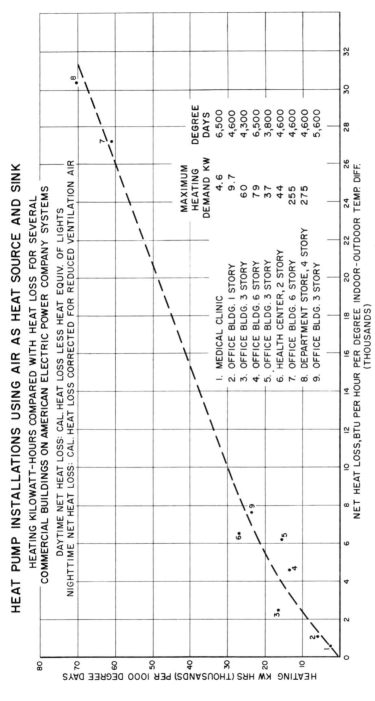

Figure 9-16 The annual heating kilowatthours of a number of heat pump installations related to the net heat loss (*ASHRAE Symposium Bulletin on Heat Pump Performance*, 1959.)

TABLE 9-8   Monthly Kilowatt and Kilowatthours for an All-Electric
Department Store in Area With about 4500 Degree Days

1. Structure	four-stories with full basement
2. Total floor area, sq ft	85,225
3. Design conditions	
Heating	70 F indoors and 10 F outdoors
Cooling	75 F indoors and 95 F outdoors
4. Calculated Heat Loss, MBtuh	
Occupied: Gross	2,875
Net (Credit for 100%	
Lights, 400 kw)	1,510
Unoccupied: Gross	2,053
5. Calculated heat gain, MBtuh	
Sensible	229
Latent	84
Total	313
6. Ventilation air, cfm	
Occupied	19,000
Unoccupied	6,330
7. Internal heat load	
Lights, kw	400
People	2,500
8. Annual energy consumption, kwhr	
Heating	216,930
Cooling	338,009
Lighting and miscellaneous	2,445,120

TABLE 9-9   Monthly Kilowatt and Kilowatthours for an All-Electric
Department Store in Area With about 4500 Degree Days

Months	Total[1] Building kw	kwh	Heat Pump[2] Heating kw	kwh	Cooling kw	kwh	Total kw	kwh	Degree Days
Sept.	656	192,960	103	864	145	38,304	145	39,168	109
Oct.	588	202,560	103	16,808	130	16,600	130	33,408	382
Nov.	588	192,960	155	20,410	72	6,950	155	27,360	622
Dec.	657	214,080	228	45,792	166	3,744	228	49,536	870
Jan.	760	217,920	311	55,008	−	−	311	55,008	963
Feb.	26	190,080	301	47,520	207	1,728	301	49,248	785
March	588	182,400	145	24,768	124	1,115	145	25,883	656
April	622	187,200	103	5,184	186	26,208	186	31,392	213
May	588	206,400	103	576	135	48,672	135	49,248	18
June	622	214,080	−	−	207	63,072	207	63,072	−
July	622	232,320	−	−	218	75,168	218	75,168	−
Aug.	656	212,160	−	−	186	56,448	186	56,448	−
Total		2,445,120		216,930		338,009		554,939	4,619

[1] Includes circulating pumps, conditioner, exhaust fans, and other accessories which are normally common to any heating and cooling distribution system.

[2] Includes refrigeration compressors and outdoor air fan motors used with heat source and sink transfer surfaces. The heat pump kilowatts represent the coincident demand at time of peak building demand.

REFERENCES

Ambrose, E. R., "Operation of Large Air Source Central Heat Pump Systems," Symposium Session on Heat Pump Performance Held at the 65th Annual Meeting of ASHRAE, Philadelphia, January 28, 1959.

ASHRAE Guide and Data Book (1964), Fundamentals and Equipment, Chap. 16, Estimating Fuel or Energy Consumption for Space Heating.

Evaluated Weather Data for Cooling Equipment Fluor Products Company, 1958.

Gilman, Stanley F., and William Clausen, Predicting Annual Heating Costs of Residental Heat Pumps, *ASHRAE Journal,* May 1959.

Hager, Nathaniel E., Jr., Estimation of Heating Energy Requirements, *ASHRAE Journal,* August 1962.

Parsons, Roger A., How to Estimate *Net* Building Space Heating Requirements, *Heating, Piping and Air Conditioning,* 155 (January 1962).

Chapter 10

Owning and Operating
Cost Evaluations

The present and future growth of a particular type of space heating and cooling application will not be determined exclusively by the interest and efforts of the respective utilities and manufacturers but will be governed to a large extent by the degree of acceptance by the general public. To get this acceptability the air conditioning installations must have a favorable competitive annual owning and operating cost.

A proper and fair evaluation can be obtained only by making a complete and accurate analysis of the design features and equipment selection together with all the other important and influencing items listed in Table 10-1, which include:

1. Capital investment of the systems being compared
2. Annual fixed charges due to the amortization and depreciation of equipment and to the interest and taxes
3. Annual operating cost of refrigeration equipment, the heating equipment, fans, pumps, and other miscellaneous equipment

CAPITAL INVESTMENT

Capital investments section of Table 10-1 should include all the equipment required for the heating and/or cooling of the structure. Frequently, in the interest of simplicity, the equipment common to the systems being compared is omitted from the tabulation. The resulting costs would, therefore, represent the differential cost between the systems. The *total cost,* of the system or systems being investigated is found by including all of the items which are an essential part of the installation.

In most instances the competitive systems being compared

182

TABLE 10-1   Annual Owning and Operating Cost Evaluation for Heating and Cooling (170-Ton Cooling)

	ELECTRIC		COMPETITIVE SYSTEM	
A. CAPITAL INVESTMENT	Heating	Cooling	Heating	Cooling
1. Electric Heating Equipment				
2. Power and Control Wiring		3,000		—
3. Controls				
4. Boilers and Auxiliary Equipment, Condensate Pumps, Motors, Storage Tanks, Fuel Piping, Etc.		—		1,332
5. Piping, Pipe Insulation, Valves, Fittings, Etc.		—		1,500
6. Ducts and Duct Insulation		—		
7. Additional Floor or Roof Area (Required for Equipment)				
8. Construction Cost - Chargeable to System		—		
9. Refrigerating Machines		25,000		27,312
10. Cooling Towers or Air-Cooled Condenser		3,500		5,700
11. Condenser Water Pumps		628		769
12. Miscellaneous				
13. Total First Cost		32,128		36,617
B. ANNUAL FIXED CHARGES				
1. Amortization and Depreciation of Equipment				
Electric Heating Equipment, Power and Control Wiring (Life same as Building)		150		
Electric Starting Equipment (20 Year Life)				
Controls (15 Year Life)				
Valves and Specialties (10 Year Life)				
Boiler and Auxiliaries, Steam and Water Piping, Fittings and Ducts (20 Year Life)				67
Duct Insulation (20 Year Life)				
Fans (15 Year Life)				
Refrigerating Machines (20 Year Life)		1,250		1,365
Cooling Towers or Air-Cooled Condenser (15 Year Life)		233		380
Water Piping, Fittings, Valves, Pumps, Insulation (20 Year Life)		31		113
Miscellaneous				
2. Interest		676		772
3. Taxes		48		55
4. Insurance and Inspection Fees (Boiler, Heating Equipment and Building)		41		47
5. Total Annual Fixed Charges		2,429		2,799
C. ANNUAL OPERATING COST				
1. Electric Power Costs		3,140		
Heating Equipment, Controls, Fan and Pump Motors, Auxiliaries				
Refrigerating Machines, Cooling Tower or Air-Cooled Condenser, Fans, Condenser Pumps, Solution Pumps, Evaporator Pumps, Purge Pumps, Auxiliaries				525
2. Fuel Cost: Gas, Steam, Oil, Coal				5,080
3. Boiler, Ducts and Piping Costs, Boiler Room Supplies, Water Treatment, Lubricating Oil and Grease, Corrosion Protection Painting, Maintenance Service (Flue, Stack, Fire Side of Boiler, Etc), Replacement of Work Parts, Make-up Water, Wages of Engineer or Operator, Janitor and Housekeeping				
4. Water - Make-up for Cooling Tower (Evaporation and Blowdown) Water Treatment		212		440
5. General Maintenance Service Cost		255		340
6. Total Annual Operating Cost		3,607		6,385
SUMMARY				
Annual Fixed Charges		2,429		2,799
Annual Operating Cost		3,607		6,385
Total Owning and Operating Cost (Today)		6,036		9,184
Total Estimated Owning and Operating Cost (10 Years Hence)				

with the electric installations are either gas, oil, or steam absorption and/or gas engine-driven equipment. It can be noted from the capital investment section that additional equipment is needed for the fossil fuel systems. Larger cooling towers or other heat sink surfaces, together with proportionally increased water flows and pumping heads are always required by the absorption machine to dissipate the approximately 30,000 Btuh/ton (compared with 15,000 Btuh/ton for the electric). This increase in cooling tower capacity, together with the larger piping and pumps, not only adds to the first cost of the absorption system, but heavier construction may be required in the structure of the building to support the additional weight.

One other item frequently overlooked in a comparative cooling analysis is the cost of the boiler and auxiliaries, which is chargeable to the cooling load, for the generation of the necessary steam for the absorption equipment. It is sometimes asserted that the boiler is needed for heating and consequently is not chargeable to cooling. This is questionable in many instances, particularly in modern office buildings where the size of the boiler will be dictated by the cooling load because of the relatively high heat gains and small heat losses. In such cases, the cooling cost must include a fair share of the amortization, interest, taxes, insurance, and maintenance of the boiler and all auxiliaries. In addition, the absorption systems must include the additional capital cost of the steam supply and return piping, condensate pump, insulation, and other such components necessary for the proper operation of the cooling system.

The disadvantages of the absorption system due to this additional equipment can be partially offset by the cost of the electric power wiring, compressor motor starters, transformers, and similar accessories needed for the electric systems. To keep the cost of these items to a minimum, a detailed layout is essential to specify correctly the location, the voltage, and the interconnection of all of the electric equipment.

ANNUAL FIXED CHARGES

The annual fixed charges, the second classification in Table 10-1, include amortization and depreciation of all equipment listed under Capital Investment, together with the applicable interest, taxes, insurance, and etc.

The expected life of the equipment, given in parentheses, are the values generally accepted by the air conditioning industry. An authoritative value for the life of the equipment is difficult to obtain because replacement is often necessary due to obsolesence. The life also will vary considerably depending upon the type of application, the geographic location, the atmospheric conditions, the quality and design of the original equipment, and upon the maintenance, service, and general overall supervision of the system.

ANNUAL OPERATING COST

The third classification given in Table 10-1 is the Annual Operating Cost. This portion of the Annual Owning and Operating Cost Evaluation requires particular attention, since it is more difficult to evaluate correctly than either of the other two classifications and is subjected to repeated examinations by all interested parties. The electric power and fuel costs will vary, depending upon size, design, and geographic location of the installation, and, consequently, separate and independent comparisons must be made in most cases.

The procedures to be followed for obtaining the power cost of electric heating and cooling systems are given in Chapter 9 and summarized in Table 9-5. The same procedures as outlined in Chapter 9, together with equation 9-2, can be used to obtain the heating fuel consumption. The design and operating data for a proper cost analysis of a steam absorption system are given by Table 10-2. The same climatological data referred to in pages 154–162 of Chapter 9 can be followed for obtaining the operation hours and ton hours of any type of cooling system. It is important to include the power cost of all of the electric auxiliaries, of the absorption equipment, such as additional cooling tower fans, and the condenser pumps, as well as the solution, evaporator, and purge pumps. The steam consumption for the refrigerating machines and kilowatthours of the auxiliaries (items 4 and 5 of Table 10-2) is multiplied by the appropriate cost and transferred to C-1 and C-2 of Table 10-1.

In figuring the kilowatthours of the auxiliaries (listed as item 5 of Table 10-2) it must be remembered that many of the absorption machine auxiliaries must operate at full demand whenever the refrigerating machine operates, regardless of the size of the cooling load. This is a disadvantage of the absorption system, since the almost continuous operation of these auxiliaries can consume a large amount of electrical energy during a cooling season.

The make-up water treatment cost for the cooling towers (including necessary blow-down to control the mineral concentration from evaporation) item C-4 of Table 10-1, will depend on the atmospheric conditions and on the chemical composition of the water. As mentioned above under Capital Investment, the absorption machines must dissipate more than twice the heat to the cooling tower as does the electric. Consequently, the cooling tower water and air quantities and the corresponding water treatment cost will be proportionally greater for the absorption machines.

The general maintenance and service costs of the boilers, cooling machines, and auxiliaries (item C-5 of Table 10-1) are sometimes difficult to correctly evaluate, but should not be overlooked in a comparative cost analysis. Several steam heating trade associations have developed a unit cost per 1000 lb of steam to cover the maintenance cost of the boiler and steam auxiliaries. A portion of the unit cost figure is chargeable to the boiler to cover such items as water treat-

TABLE 10-2   Design and Operating Data Required for Cost Analysis of
Steam Absorption Cooling Systems

	Refrigerating Load Percent of Full			
	¼	½	¾	Full
1. Operating hours				
2. Tons				
3. Ton-hours				
4. Refrigerating machines Steam: Lb per ton-hour* Total				
Kwhr: Per ton† Total				
5. Kwhr of auxiliaries Condenser pumps				
Cooling tower pump				
Solution pump				
Evaporator pump				
Purge pump				
Miscellaneous				
6. Water make-up for cooling tower, gal				

Note: 1) Operating hours (1) and corresponding refrigerant load (2) obtained
         from data in Chapter 9.
      2) Cooling tower make-up water includes evaporation and blowdown.
         Normally taken at 5.4 gal per ton-hour for absorption and 2.6 gal
         per ton-hour for electric drive.
      3) Steam* and Electric Energy† Consumption at the given operat-
         ing conditions can be obtained from manufacturers' published data.

ment, boiler room supplies, maintenance, water cost, etc., and the
remaining amount covers similar services for the boiler auxiliaries.
In most instances, local heating contractors are prepared to offer
a service contract to cover this work.

The maintenance cost of the refrigerating machine, together

with the auxiliaries, will also vary in different localities. Many service organizations agree that the annual maintenance cost of a motor-driven refrigeration unit will be lower than for a comparable absorption machine. The extent of this saving will depend, however, on the equipment design and on the geographic location. In many of the smaller cities and towns the local service organizations are not qualified to service the larger absorption equipment. Consequently, the service must be obtained from other areas which may be several hundred miles away. This means that the travel time of the service personnel will add considerably to the service cost. Generally, the manufacturer, the local utility or an independent service organization will arrange for a preventative maintenance and service contract on either type of equipment. If at all possible, the cost of this type of contract should be included in the annual owning and operating cost evaluation.

COST EVALUATION EXAMPLE (*Using Table 10-1*)

An example of the recommended cost evaluation procedure for a typical 170-ton space cooling installation is given in Table 10-1. The evaluation is based on the following costs and assumptions:

1. Taxes at 15 mills
2. Insurance at 1.27 percent
3. Gas. 72 cents/1000 cu ft; consumption of 4690 cu ft/hr for 1500 hr
4. Electricity. Absorption system auxiliaries, 17.5 kw for 2000 hr at 1.6 cents per kwhr; refrigeration compressor, 131 kw demand for 1500 hours operation at 1.6 cents per kwhr
5. Water. 32 cents per 1000 gal, including 40 percent sewer tax; consumption (evaporation and blowdown) for absorption 5.4 gal/ton-hour, for electric 2.6 gal/ton-hour
6. Water treatment cost not included

It is to be noted that the analysis includes only items which differ according to type of refrigeration used. It therefore shows the cost difference between the two systems, but is not the total cost of either system.

The comparison in Table 10-1 indicates that the expected annual owning and operating cost of a 170-ton absorption system will be 3148 dollars or 52 percent higher than for a comparable electric driven system based on the gas, water, electricity, and other costs used in the example. The necessity to reject about twice the amount of heat per ton-hour from the absorption cycle means appreciably larger heat transfer surfaces, condenser pumps, water lines and cooling tower. This additional equipment is reflected in the initial cost and the operating cost of the absorption system.

It is to be noted that the operating cost of all auxiliaries of the absorption system, such as the 1½ to 7½ hp solution pump, 1½ to 5 hp evaporator pump and the 2 hp purge pump must be included in the evaluation. The air conditioning contractor's price generally includes only the furnishing and installing of the absorption refrigeration machine. The foundation pads for the equipment must be supplied by others. Similarly, the magnetic starters for the pumps, as well as all the interconnecting wiring between the pump and the machine panel board, must be furnished and installed by others. In addition to the absorption refrigeration unit, the steam lines to the generator flanges of the machine, the condensate traps, pressure-reducing valves, cooling tower and condenser, bypass valves as well as capacity control valves must be furnished and installed by others. The cost of these and all other such auxiliaries must be included as part of the capital investment.

GAS TURBINE AND INTERNAL COMBUSTION ENGINES

The comparative analysis illustrated by Table 10-1 is based on an electrically driven centrifugal compressor and a steam absorption machine with the same cooling capacity. The equipment selection and costs were based on 1964 data from several manufacturers. The size and design of the installation, together with the different possible equipment selections, can make a material difference in the results of a comparative owning and operating cost analysis. The suggested procedure, therefore, is not intended to show the merits of a particular type of equipment but only to indicate how such an evaluation can be made.

The logical choice for a cooling system of 100 tons and above would normally be between a steam absorption machine and a motor-driven centrifugal unit. There are other possible selections, however, including the gas engine drive, diesel engine drive, and the gas turbine drive connected to a conventional vapor compression refrigeration machine. The same procedure outlined in Table 10-1 can be used in the evaluation of any of these systems. Many of the deterrent factors mentioned in connection with absorption equipment will apply equally to other fossil fuel systems. In addition they have several other disadvantages. Motor-driven air conditioning equipment has been used by the thousands during the past 30 years and is very reliable. In contrast, gas engine drives are relatively new but are being vigorously promoted by gas interests and engine manufacturers. Such engines have a higher first cost and maintenance cost when compared with an electric motor. They must have almost continuous maintenance by a skilled mechanic, including frequent major engine overhauls, engine tuneups and ignition system adjustments, like any other internal combustion engine. The exhaust gas from the engine must be vented to the outside, combustion air must be provided, the noise level is high and the engine has an extremely short life when compared with an electric motor. Even in spite of these disadvantages, gas engine-driven refrigeration machines may have a lower owning and operating cost than many of the other units, when full advantage is taken of the jacket heat loss for comfort space heating and domestic water heating and when a relatively low fuel rate, such as is found in parts of the natural gas area, is available.

The gas turbine drive is also a relatively new application. The gas turbine, in this case, is a stationary version of the aircraft turboprop jet. Air is compressed, mixed with fuel, and burned in a combustion chamber. Part of the exhaust gas passes through a turbine wheel to drive the air compressor, and the remainder passes through another turbine wheel to drive the output shaft. The thermal efficiency is in the neighborhood of only 18 percent if work is not salvaged from the exhaust gas. This cycle efficiency is quite low because considerable energy must be expended to compress large quantities of air for complete combustion. In addition, if gas at 150 psig is not available, a gas compressor is also required.

The basic objectives of the gas turbine type of application are to generate electricity and to recover the heat energy from the exhaust gas (at a temperature of 800 to 900 F) by means of a waste heat boiler which provides space heating, domestic water heating and absorption cooling. The expected optimum efficiency, if all the loads can be simultaneously used, is in the order of 30 to 35 percent. As illustrated by the duration curves (Chapter 9), full heating and cooling capacity is only required for a very short period of time. Consequently, it can be safely assumed that the steam requirements for many installations will not match the available waste heat capacity from the gas turbine. It is therefore necessary to provide an exhaust heat bypass around the waste heat boiler in order to take care of the substantial periods of oversupply of waste heat.

A further disadvantage of the gas turbine application is the adverse effect of the ambient temperature on the performance. The available power and heating capacity of gas turbines declines with an increase in the temperature of the inlet air. A reduction of 23 percent can be expected, for instance, if the temperature of the inlet air changes from 40 to 120 F. Consequently, the air for the turbine must be passed through a washer and filter in order to keep its temperature and purity to an acceptable level during the summer months.

It is usually conceded by all authoritative sources that the first cost of a gas turbine and associated equipment is and for some time to come will be higher than comparable electric equipment operated with purchased power. The chief hope of the gas industry for a more favorable competitive position, therefore, is to have a sufficiently lower operating cost to overcome this first cost disadvantage. This can only be brought about by allocating a substantial part of the capital and operating cost to the by-product service such as heating, cooling, domestic water and etc.

In recent times, cost of the small, independent, electric power generation plants has not been notably successful in competing with purchased power. This is because electric utilities serve widely diversified loads and therefore can operate at efficiencies impossible in small isolated plants. In addition, purchased power is usually abundant, reliable, and reasonable in cost. Consequently, the trend has been moving toward the elimination of the small central boiler room concept.

Considerably more factual information is therefore required before the merits of such a gas turbine application can be accurately determined. Its feasibility and acceptance are highly questionable, because basically it is still a central station boiler approach to energy application with all the traditional problems of administration, supervision, upkeep, and maintenance.

ENERGY COSTS OF THE FUTURE

A true energy cost analysis should not be limited to present day prices but must be projected 5 to 10 years or more into the future to get a true representative operating cost of various systems during their expected life.

Generally overlooked in most energy cost comparisons is the improved position of electric energy resulting from the continuing and cumulative increases in the cost of competitive fuels. This is illustrated in Figure 10-1 which shows the retail price index of fuels and electricity for 1935 through 1964, using 1947–1949 as a base of 100. It can be noted that during the 10-year period, from 1954 to 1964, the retail price index of gas has risen about 14 percent and

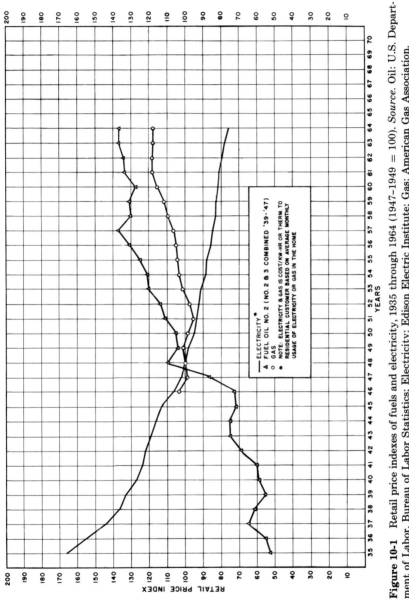

Figure 10-1 Retail price indexes of fuels and electricity, 1935 through 1964 (1947–1949 = 100). *Source.* Oil: U.S. Department of Labor, Bureau of Labor Statistics; Electricity: Edison Electric Institute; Gas: American Gas Association.

oil about 19 percent. In contrast, the average electricity cost has
decreased about 12 percent for the country as a whole. What is even
more important is that every development points toward a continua-
tion of this trend in energy costs. It is significant that the electric
power industry, largest users of fossil fuel, continue to make notable
improvements in cost of their power generation, transmission and
distribution so that there is a solid basis for believing that the
industry can retain and even improve this favorable trend.

In Figure 10-1 the curves for electricity and gas represent the
cost per kilowatthour or therm to residential customers, based on
the total average monthly use in the home. In comparison the composite average oil retail price index is based upon data collected by
the U.S. Department of Labor, Bureau of Labor Statistics, from
46 index cities such as Atlanta, Chicago, New York, Pittsburgh,
Minneapolis, San Francisco and other fairly large cities.

Such average retail price indexes are useful to show the cost
trend in the nation as a whole. It will be found, however, that the
actual fuel and electricity prices for a particular geographic area
vary considerably from these average prices. Consequently, comparative operating costs of electric energy and competitive fuels
must be based both on the present day prices and on the past and
future trends for the particular area under consideration.

COMPARATIVE ENERGY COST (*Heating*)

The composite average retail fuel price indexes, shown in Figure
10-1, can materially effect the relative energy costs of electricity,
gas, oil and coal. Such indexes indicate the average trend of the
entire country and may not be indicative of a particular area. For
this reason, in making a specific evaluation it is advisable to compute
the relative energy cost based on local prices by using the equation:

$$C = \frac{100 \times u}{h \times E_s} \tag{10-1}$$

where
C = million Btu for 1 dollar
u = unit cost: cents/cu ft for gas
                                      cents/gal for oil
                                      cents/kwhr for electricity
h = heat content per unit: 1000 Btu/cu ft for gas
                                      140,000 Btu/gal for oil
                                      3413 Btu/kwhr for electricity

E_s = overall seasonal operating efficiency
   = 60 percent for gas
   = 55 percent for oil
   = 100 percent for electricity
   = 250 to 400 percent for heat pump

Either electric resistance heating, heat pumps, gas, steam, oil, or coal may prove to have the lowest energy cost for a particular heating application. The selection of the most practical energy source should only be made after carefully considering all of the influencing factors.

The comparative heating energy cost of electric resistance, heat pump, gas, central plant steam, and oil is shown in chart form in Figure 10-2 and in tabular form in Table 10-3.

The effect of the change in retail prices on the relative cost of the different form of heat energy is perhaps best illustrated by Figure 10-2. The millions Btu obtainable for 1 dollar is indicated on this figure by the intersection of unit cost of the energy (on the vertical axis) and the corresponding curves A, B, C, D or E. The heavy broken lines on Figure 10-2 demonstrate the procedure for

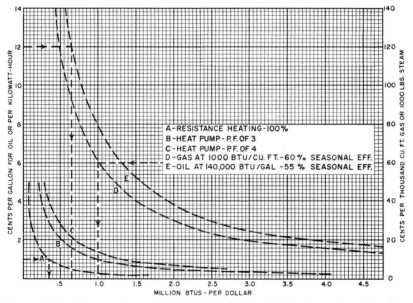

Figure 10-2 Comparative energy cost chart showing the heating cost, million Btus per dollar.

TABLE 10-3

	Million Btu for $1	$/Million Btu
Electric Resistance: 1 cent/kwhr	0.34	$2.93
2 cents/kwhr	0.17	5.86
Heat Pump (PF-3)		
1 cent /kwhr	1.02	0.98
2 cents/kwhr	0.51	1.96
Heat Pump (PF-4)		
1 cent/kwhr	1.36	0.74
2 cents/kwhr	0.68	1.47
Gas, 1000 Btu/cu ft:		
60 cent/1000 cu ft	1.0	1.0
80 cent/1000 cu ft	0.75	1.33
Oil, 140,000 Btus/gal:		
10 cent/gal	0.77	1.30
15 cent/gal	0.51	1.95

finding the energy cost for 1 cent per kilowatt energy, 60 cent per 1000 cu ft gas and 12 cent per gal oil.

SEASONAL OPERATING EFFICIENCY (*Fuel Burning Efficiency*)

In the energy cost comparison given by Figure 10-2 and Table 10-3 a seasonal operating efficiency of 60 percent was used for a gas heating system and of 55 percent for an oil system. This is much lower than the catalogue efficiency of 80 percent which is sometimes advocated by a number of manufacturers and trade associations for this type of equipment.

The so-called catalogue efficiency, which is in reality a "boiler test efficiency" under controlled conditions, will seldom, if ever, be obtained on actual installations. There is a significant difference between this boiler test efficiency and the desired seasonal operating efficiency. To obtain the boiler test efficiency, the boiler is cleaned on both the fire side and the water side, before it is put on a predetermined load (usually its rated capacity) and operated for at least 24 hours before taking readings. During this warm-up period, the air-fuel ratio is adjusted to give maximum efficiency. It is apparent that such tests do not simulate actual operating conditions throughout the season, since such influencing factors as the stand-by and distribution system losses, previously mentioned, together with the possible faulty operation of the boiler have been excluded. It is for this reason that the actual seasonal efficiency, which should be used in the annual operating cost evaluation will be much lower than the 80 percent ideal test efficiency usually given in the manufacturers' catalogues for fuel burning package boilers.

Usually a fuel heating system, in comparison with electric, is exceedingly limited and inflexible in its application. For instance, the fuel system for safety reasons must generally be remotely located from the heated space, since a flame is ever present, and a vent is always necessary. This necessitates an indirect system in which case the fuel heats a fluid (air, water, or steam) that in turn is circulated to the space to be heated. As a consequence, the losses in this transfer of heat from one medium to another must all be charged to the annual energy consumption of a fuel system, together with heat wasted up the stack and to the unoccupied areas; the stand-by and combustion losses (of piping and other heat handling equipment), and the adverse effect caused by the depreciation and corrosion of the equipment. Some engineers use the so-called boiler efficiencies given in the manufacturers' catalogues for making operating cost analyses and, as a result, their fuel consumption estimates are often too low and misleading.

It was pointed out in Chapter 9 that the heating equipment, as well as the cooling equipment, operates at 100 percent capacity for a relatively small percentage of the time, a fact which also adversely effects the overall seasonal operating efficiency of fuel burning equipment. It is therefore difficult to estimate the seasonal operating efficiency and to predict accurately the energy consumption of fuel burning equipment. The available data indicates, however, that a realistic seasonal efficiency for fuel burning equipment will range from 50 to 65 percent depending upon the various design and application factors.

DESIGN AND OPERATION CHARACTERISTICS

The retail fuel prices indexes and the equivalent heat energy costs are not the only determining factors for the public acceptance of a particular type of heating and cooling system. The many possible economic reductions in the heating and cooling requirements as well as the maximum utilization of the inherent and desirable design and application characteristics play an important part in the final selection.

A discussion of a number of the possible heat conservation

devices and methods (to reduce the heating and cooling requirements) such as thermal insulation application, multiple-glazed windows and doors, and infiltration and ventilation reduction is given in Chapter 6. Insulation and multiple glazed windows and doors, of course, can be used irrespective of the type of heating and cooling systems employed. Generally, however, considerably more insulation can be economically justified with electric heating than with fossil fuel systems. This additional thermal barrier does not necessarily penalize the electric system, because the lower initial cost of electric heating will usually more than offset the cost of additional insulation. Therefore, the electric installation can still be in a favorable first cost position and, at the same time, the energy cost will be more competitive with fuel systems. A summary of 14 design and application characteristics of electric heating and cooling equipment which should be considered in an owning and operating cost evaluation, is listed in Table 10-4. A major advantage of electric resistance heating and the heat pump is the comfort and flexibility (item 6 of Table 10-4) provided by in-the-room heating and cooling. The economic advantage to be gained by generating the heating and the cooling effect at the point of use is excellently demonstrated by such applications as schools, motels, and apartments.

Classrooms are particularly attractive for this type of installation. Most classrooms are only occupied 7 to 9 hours per day and 5 days per week, exclusive of legal holidays and the extended vacations at Christmas and Easter which represent 20 to 25 percent of the school year. During this relatively short period, a 72 to 75 F indoor temperature is generally maintained, and a predetermined amount of ventilation air is used. Even so, the conduction and ventilation air heat loss, during this occupied period, is offset to a considerable extent by the lights, people, and solar effect. Generally, no heat at all is needed at outdoor temperatures of about 40 F or higher, and instead some form of cooling must be provided to prevent overheating in the classrooms. In addition, a further reduction in the annual heating requirement can be realized by holding an indoor temperature of 50 to 55 F during the remaining 75 to 80 percent, unoccupied period of the school year.

With such widely variable heating loads, the design capacity of the system is very seldom required, and actually most of the time only 25 percent or even less of the rated capacity is needed. It is, therefore, quite obvious that fuel-fired heating and cooling equipment remotely located in a boiler room and connected to a network of cold and hot water or steam piping, with the accompanying high

TABLE 10-4   Design and Application Characteristics of Electric Heating and Cooling Which Should Be Considered in an Owning and Operating Cost Evaluation

(1) FIRST COST. The equipment is frequently more economical to install than competitive fuels and the resulting savings will offset, to a considerable extent, the additional cost of insulation used to reduce the structure heat loss. By combining heating and cooling in the same equipment it is possible to improve the economics of both cycles.

(2) INFILTRATION AIR. The additional insulation, generally used, results in a tighter building construction with a corresponding reduction in outdoor infiltration air and an increase in humidity level. Further reduction is realized by eliminating the needed outdoor air to support combustion of fuel boilers.

(3) BOILERS, BOILER ROOM AND CHIMNEY. This equipment, along with circulating pumps, heat exchangers, connecting water and steam piping, and other accessories used with fuel burning equipment, are eliminated from the premises.

(4) SAFETY—QUIETNESS. No danger of violent failures, asphyxiation from carbon monoxide and other gases, and no fuel leakage or improper adjustment. The combustion noise and vibration are also eliminated.

(5) CLEANLINESS—HEALTHFULNESS. All kinds of oily film residue, flue deposits, smoke, flame and fumes are eliminated. Cleaning costs, janitor expenses, painting costs, housekeeping chores can be drastically reduced.

(6) COMFORT—FLEXIBILITY. Heat only when and where needed. Each room or space heated independently with own thermostat to give accurate control, regardless of location. Such flexibility in any other type of system is more costly because of expensive controls, motor valves, etc. Room may be added in future without expensive heating plant expansion. Location of heating and cooling equipment not fixed, can be placed in basement, on roof, or practically any place in the building.

(7) BUILDING COST. Eliminating of boiler, fuel storage facilities, chimney, auxiliaries, and in many cases an extra building, saves floor space and reduces construction cost, particularly in commercial installations. The combination of heating and cooling into a single system results in a minimum use of space.

(8) MAINTENANCE AND SERVICE. Service labors and operating difficulties usually are materially reduced. No boiler or pump replacements. Eliminates possible freeze-ups from possible boiler breakdowns. Services of operating engineers, required in some areas, are no longer needed.

(9) HEAT LOSSES FROM DISTRIBUTION SYSTEM. Generating the heat at the point of use eliminates extensive loss of heat energy through trenches, piping and ductwork. No energy wasted during off-cycle and no standby losses. Steam or hot water circulation is eliminated along with accompanying heat loss through piping.

(10) SUMMER AIR CONDITIONING. The electric power facilities are suitable for summer air conditioning. Either central system or unit conditioner readily adaptable.

(11) PARTIAL LOAD. Operating cost of equipment remains constant, even at partial load in contrast to fuel fired equipment.

(12) LONGER LIFE. Lack of corrosion and wearing out of parts extends the life of the major equipment to that of the building.

(13) FUEL PRICES. Fuel prices have been and will continue to increase, in some areas at a very rapid and consistent rate, while electricity is holding firm.

(14) CONCENTRATION OF UTILITY SERVICE. By combining heating and cooling into a single all year-round system, it is possible to have the building operate on a single electrical utility service. Thus the need for gas, oil or coal is eliminated.

stand-by losses from the boiler, from the stack, and from the piping will result in an exceedingly low overall seasonal operating efficiency. In contrast, the electric heating and cooling units, located within the occupied space will not only eliminate all such losses and inefficiencies but in addition can often be installed at a lower initial cost.

The same favorable consideration which is cited for electric heating and cooling of classrooms applies to motels, apartments and many other commercial and industrial installations where practical and positive independent control of individual areas is mandatory.

Impressive savings are frequently realized from the design and application features for electric heating and cooling listed in Table 10-4. More importantly, the architect or consulting engineer need no longer be concerned with the boiler room, chimney, piping, trenches, crawl spaces, and associated physical and mechanical considerations of conventional wet heat systems. The building can literally be designed around the extraordinary flexibility of the electric system. Merely to substitute electric heating for a steam or hot water boiler, for instance, in a given structure, is certainly not the proper procedure and, if followed, will frequently be disappointing in both the initial and the operating cost.

Instead, the design features and application practices covered by the previous chapters, if followed, will result in a very acceptable and satisfactory electric heating and air conditioning installation. All pertinent factors which will influence the selection of the utility services should be considered. Only by a complete and fair evaluation of all of these factors can a decision be reached as to the most practical total owning and operating cost for the present and for the years to come.

REFERENCES

Hersbey, C. R., Old and New Values in Space Heating, *ASHRAE Journal,* October 1963.
Little, Philip F., Which Drive for Your Heat Pump, *Actual Specifying Engineering,* December 1961.
Readers' Forum, *Electric Heating Journal,* August 1964.
Rickert, Paul H., The True Facts About Flame Heating System Efficiencies, *Electric Heating Journal,* December 1963, January and February 1964.
Szabo, B. S., Heat Pumps Up North, *Air Conditioning, Heating and Ventilating,* September, 1964.

Index